CAN I HELP YOU?

The Adventure of a Praying Man

TOM BORGA

urbanpress

Can I Help You?
by Tom Borga
Copyright ©2022 Tom Borga

ISBN 978-1-63360-195-6

For Worldwide Distribution
Printed in the U.S.A.

Urban Press
P.O. Box 8881
Pittsburgh, PA 15221-0881
412.646.2780
www.urbanpress.us

DEDICATION

To The One Who Helps

Matthew 7: 7 & 8

"Ask and it will be given to you; seek, and you will find; knock, and it will be opened to you.

For everyone who asks receives, and he who seeks finds, and to him who knocks it will be opened."

Bless you,

Tom Borga

OCTOBER 1, 2022

INTRODUCTION

God is looking for you. He wants to help you. You may think you don't need help, but honestly, you along with everyone else are always in need.

I was nearing the end of a long career when this story showed up. I needed this story because I needed some help. I needed an adventure to remind me of some things I had forgotten.

Some of the most intimate, inspiring, and miraculous but true moments of my life are chronicled throughout this volume, but these memories were finally penned because a new friend appeared.

This new friend reminded me of the components of true love and the intimacy that prayer has to offer.

Come along on my adventure which weaves autobiographical fact and fanciful fiction that promises to spark your curiosity.

Let the adventure begin.

"I will lift up my eyes to the mountains;
from where shall my help come from?"
(Psalm 121:1, NASB).

"YES,
CAN I HELP YOU?"

Have you ever had "truth" sneak up and blindside you, and you found yourself in a new place?

For me, it all began one day when and where I least expected it. I was outside my home on the back deck of my house. Our deck area has a patio table and four chairs surrounded by plants. My wife has plants everywhere. Each spring, Crystal, my wife, plants flowers that surround our house — in the back, in the front, and on the sides. I am not sure I ever really appreciated the beauty of our surroundings until that afternoon.

I was working at home, fatigued from being in front of my laptop all day and haggling with customers and fellow employees over orders gone awry or pushing quotations out the door, hoping to create some new business. I have been a salesman of commercial lighting products for 38 years with the same company. Most of that time, I made a good living, but this year had been a little different. I struggled to make ends meet, and found myself worrying about the future.

I'm 64 years old, and I have no money saved for retirement. I had spent all my 401(k) money on family emergencies, repairs to my house, or helping us through the lean months that can occur when a salesman depends on his commissions. My wife isn't employed because we decided early in our marriage that it was more important for Crystal to be at home, and frankly we never felt we needed the extra income. However lately, I was feeling the pressure of it all.

That's when the adventure began.

I took a break and plodded out the back door to get a breath of fresh air when my wife whispered excitedly, "Look, a praying mantis!" On one of her plants toward the back of the deck was a triangular headed insect posing for us. He was atop a dark pink flower blooming perfectly in balance with his eerily poised and still stick body. To capture this sight, Crystal took out her phone, and just as she was taking the photo, the mantis turned its head toward us. We got a perfect photo of this fascinating creature staring at us, as if to say, "Yes, can I help you?"

We were so excited to catch this event that we spent the next few minutes looking at the photos rather than watching the mantis' next move. When we turned back to the plant, he was gone. We would have loved to have seen where he ventured off to; we had never seen a praying mantis amongst the flowers before.

My wife used the picture as her phone screensaver, and I made sure I saved a copy to show off. We figured that was the end of Mr. Mantis.

I went downstairs into my office, closed my

lap-top, and put away the day's work. We went on with our normal routine of dinner, clean-up, some television, and prayer before bedtime. Tomorrow would be another typically long day; I was glad to be in bed early.

2

QUITE A DAY

I try to get up before the rest of my household (my wife and 23-year-old daughter) so I can have some quiet time with God. I love to spend time in prayer and do some Bible reading, getting my heart and mind in a good place. That isn't always easy to do when life is swirling with distractions, but when I succeed it is always beneficial.

This particular day, however, I failed. I got up early, but was distracted by an email I didn't answer from the day before. By the time I formulated an answer, got back to the customer, emptied the dishwasher, and put on some coffee, it was time to get to an appointment that required sitting in traffic for an hour. The later I left, the worse it would be, so I decided to listen to the Bible on my phone while driving. Maybe I could enjoy some productive prayer time in traffic.

As I was leaving, I decided to look out back and see if there was any sign of Mr. Mantis. I knew it was a long shot, but I couldn't get yesterday's picture out of my mind. Many of the flowers were just beginning to open in the morning sun, but there was no sign of our friend. Oh well, after all, I was in a hurry, so it was off to the races.

I got into my 2006 Toyota Sienna, a minivan which comes in handy when I need to make a delivery. I sell lighting products to businesses and contractors, so when an emergency order comes in, I may have to load up the van and deliver it myself. I was backing out of my driveway as I connected my phone to the hands-free dashboard device and turned on my favorite Bible app.

I slowly backed down the driveway, looking through the rear-view mirror as I went, when I saw him — Mr. Mantis. He was on top of the fence that led to my backyard, sitting backwards with his head turned to me just like the day before. I went back another ten feet, parked at the bottom of the driveway, and ran back up to see him as fast as I could.

When I got there, he was gone! I opened the gate to the fence and feverishly looked around, but there was no mantis! *Maybe I thought I saw him, maybe I saw something else.*

I went back to the car and drove off to my appointment, paying no attention to the Gospel of John on my Bible app. My brain was trying to figure out if I had really seen that insect or not.

I was soon distracted by the traffic as I merged onto I-75, and shortly moved into the new toll express lane. It costs a few more dollars that I wasn't sure I had, but it certainly saves time. I was on my way to Buckhead, which is a wealthy part of Atlanta with nice hotels, high-rise condominiums, and big business. The business district is a short distance from the Georgia governor's mansion and large luxurious homes for the rich and famous.

At one time, I got a lot of business from this area. I still had some, but my portfolio had dwindled in recent years. I sold to property managers, maintenance engineers, and supervisors who bought lighting for their buildings.

For the most part, I really enjoy my work, but being in sales can be stressful. I was given goals and this year I had only met my goal for one month, falling short every other month. It was the middle of September, and I was concerned about the deficit in my sales. All these things were on my mind as I entered a parking garage, got my ticket to park, and proceeded to see my customer.

I love going out to see customers and taking them to lunch. I get to know them better and have developed great friendships that have lasted for years. I went to see two different customers, then proceeded to go see my friend, Eddie, who I've known for twenty years. He's worked for three different property management companies and has called me to help him wherever he moves.

I was supposed to take him to lunch, so after helping him with a lighting order, we prepared to go to a nearby restaurant, when my phone blew up with emails regarding a big sales problem that had me worried. I got several emails from one of my biggest customers along with one of his other vendors for which we had a custom lighting fixture made. I asked Eddie if he would excuse me today because I needed to get back to my office and deal with this issue. Eddie understood, and I was back in my car to shuffle through the traffic and sit down at my desk.

But before I got back, I got a direct call from my customer:

"Tom, we have a big problem. Those 300 custom fixtures you had made for our millworker don't work. You forgot a plug on both ends so that several of them could be connected. You're going to have to have these re-worked, and we have very little time. How are you going to do this?"

I told him I would investigate the details and get back to him. I reassured him that we would do everything possible to correct this. Although I was clueless on what to do next, I knew there must be an answer. My customer trusted me, so at least we got this initial uncomfortable conversation out of the way. Now I had to figure it out.

Almost back at my office, my mind reviewed the situation. I needed to look at the details, review the initial design, call the millworker, call the manufacturer, call my boss, look at costs, look at the time frame involved, and on and on. Details and questions were circling my brain like a carousel: I couldn't believe this was happening. This custom order was one of the few good things that had happened this year. I thought I was so clever — I came up with an answer to a problem we were trying to solve for a couple of years, but instead of me being a hero, it could turn out to be a disaster.

I said a prayer: "Lord, what's going on here? Why did this go sour? I felt like You were guiding me to this solution for my customer. How could this have gone so wrong? Please help me through this in a way that works for my customer and isn't devastating financially for my company or me. Amen."

I went into my local office and warehouse and sought assistance from the project managers who had been working on this account. The next five hours were filled with emails, conversations, and more questions. As it was closing in on 6:00 p.m., there was still much to be done, but I was spent. I needed to go home.

As I was driving home, Crystal called me, "Where are you, honey? Dinner is on the table."

"I'm on the way home; I'll be there soon."

"How was your day? Did you sell any light bulbs?" (She asks that every day, thinking it's funny.)

"It was quite a day. I'll tell you when I get in."

"You don't sound too good, maybe I can cheer you up. Guess who I saw today?"

"I don't have a clue; can we talk about this when I get home?"

"I thought it would cheer you up, but if you don't want to . . ."

"Alright, who did you see today?"

"Your friend on the flower."

"You mean the praying mantis? Then I'm not crazy. I saw him this morning on the fence on the side of the house as I was pulling out. Where did you see him?"

"He was on the front porch when I was watering the planters, but I only saw him for a second, then he disappeared. He's a funny little fellow."

"Yes, he is. Okay, I'm pulling up the driveway. Be there in a second."

I pulled up, got out of the car, and looked around, just in case Mr. Mantis appeared. Despite all that had occurred at work, I couldn't think about anything but that insect.

3

THE ENCOUNTER

The next morning, I was awakened by a ding from my phone since I forgot to turn my phone off before bedtime. A ding meant I had an email. I looked at the clock and it was 6:00 a.m. Who would be emailing me at 6:00 a.m.? It's probably spam. Unfortunately I was wrong. It was a millworker passing along a time frame not to my liking. I had two weeks to get those fixtures back to the manufacturer, fix the problem, and have them returned. If that didn't happen, it would delay the construction of ten new retail stores and the possibility of them blaming us for the delay, which could mean a huge financial responsibility or losing the customer. I quickly showered and flew out the door. I would have to go to the office and talk to my warehouse about having a company pick-up those fixtures and ship them directly to the manufacturer ASAP.

As I went out the side door, I heard a voice, "Hi

Neighbor, what's the hurry?" I looked around and shook my head, thinking I was hearing voices. Then once again, "Hey Tom, wait a second."

There was a lot going on inside me, but not to the extent that I was hearing voices. I opened the car door, and then I saw him. At the top of the fence was Mr. Mantis. But this time, he was looking right at me. I shut the door and walked up to the fence, and with my eyes locked on his, I thought, "If Mr. Mantis just talked to me, I'm running the other way!"

I focused on him as he seemed to turn his head and blink a few times. "Did you just talk to me?"

Again, he seemed to blink and cocked his head in the other direction. We stared at each other in silence and then I turned around and mumbled, "Just as I thought . . . "

"Thought what? What did you think?"

I froze. I turned slowly thinking he would be gone, and then I would turn around and drive as fast as I could to my office, forgetting the whole episode. But he was still there, and as I walked closer, I saw his little mouth open, "I wasn't talking to the fence, Thomas, I'm talking to you!"

"You are not talking to me! Insects don't talk, at least not in human language, not in my language, not in real life!"

"Sorry, but I'm talking to you right now in your language in real life. Would you like me to talk in another language; I know several!"

I was dumbfounded, but also curious. *I must be crazy!* I blinked, rubbed my eyes, massaged my temples, and looked again, "Sorry to be redundant, but are you, a praying mantis, talking to me, a human being?"

Without hesitation, "Yes, I am, and I'm concerned about you."

"Well, I'm concerned about me too. How's this happening?"

"That's not what I meant; I'm concerned about your emotional state. You were flying out the door. I had to stop you."

"You wouldn't understand. I've messed up on a project at work and I have to get it fixed."

He sat back lifting his front legs in his typical praying stance, "If you'll just wait, I can help you."

Normally, I would have been trying to get this problem taken care of as soon as possible so I could focus on my other sales. At that moment, I couldn't think of anything to do but talk to this creature. "How can you possibly help me?"

"By teaching you how to wait. I've found that human beings don't like to wait."

"True, but sometimes there's no time to wait, sometimes things need to be taken care of fast or your customer's going to make you pay for the construction delay of ten new stores!"

"Look, all I'm saying is to stop for a second and pray. I'm a praying mantis, you know."

"Yes, but I thought that name was just because of the way your legs come together as if praying."

"As if praying? What do you think I'm doing the whole time as I wait for hours and sometimes longer for some food to come by?"

"Praying?"

"Absolutely, I'm praying for my daily bread, and thanking God for my next meal before it even happens. He knows what your need is even before you ask."

"I've read that before; you know I read the Bible almost every day."

"Did you read it today?"

"No, but . . ."

"But, what? Did you know that he who waits on the Lord shall renew their strength? They will mount up with wings like eagles. They will walk and not be weary, they will run and will not faint."

"Thank you, Mr. Mantis. That's Isaiah 40:31. So, I guess I need to heed what I read."

"Exactly. Let's give this a try. Let's wait on the Lord for a minute, pray together, and see if this wait brings clarity. God can go before us and set things in motion."

"Good idea." For the next five minutes we prayed about the situation. I was asking God to do what only He could do. We both believed that God had the answers.

This was unbelievable, I was talking and praying and learning to "wait on God" with an insect. I really felt like God was listening, however, so I waited and prayed with my new friend until I felt God had it under control. I realized that I was helpless without God's guidance.

I opened my eyes and Mr. Mantis was gone, and I was wondering again if this was all real.

4

THE FOLLOW-UP

As I got into my car, I realized that a key to accomplishing the re-work of those fixtures was the speed of retrieval from the millworker to the manufacturer. Instead of waiting until I got to the office, I called George, my warehouse manager. Surprisingly, he had already requested a pickup based on our conversations from the day before, but I didn't remember asking him to do that.

Then I called the manufacturer and got right through to the owner of this mid-sized manufacturer, which was a minor miracle. He informed me that my boss had already called him a few minutes earlier and asked for a favor: The owner promised a fast turn-around, and I hung up the phone dumbfounded.

Everything that could be done at this time was already accomplished without me having to lift a finger. Mr. Mantis' words came back to me "God can go before us and set things in motion." All I could do was laugh and thank the Lord. I was so thankful, and so joyful that I couldn't stop laughing.

But then, more of Mr. Mantis' words came back to me. "Hey, Tom, wait a second." And then, "I wasn't talking to the fence, Thomas." He had used my name. How did he know my name? I had to go back and find him. If I had not imagined him, then, I had to know how he knew my name.

Now that this major work problem was moving forward toward a solution, I turned the car around and went back to the house. I thought, *I'll work at home today and if I happen to see Mr. Mantis, then I would know he wasn't a figment of my imagination.*

As soon as I got out of the van, I looked on the fence, but there was no mantis. I went to the backyard and looked around, especially around the flowers. When I was on the porch looking through those flowers, Crystal opened the back door and surprised me, "What are you doing home?"

"Oh nothing. I just decided to work at home today." Then, deflecting the questions, I asked her, "What are you doing out here?"

"What do you think, silly? I've got a watering can in my hand. I'm watering the flowers before it gets too hot today. It's supposed to get to 100 degrees; you would think it was July and not September. Hey look, Mr. Mantis is back!"

"Where?" I exclaimed, with a little too much excitement.

"Take it easy, Darling, it's just an insect. He's right there where he was when we first saw him, on the Impatiens."

"On the what?"

"On the Impatiens, the New Guinea Impatiens;

that's the name of the flower. But maybe it should be your name lately. You sure have been a bit touchy, saying you have been impatient is putting it mildly. Are you okay?"

"I am now; hey look, he's moving."

Mr. Mantis was walking across the Impatiens to the next flowerpot. I had no idea what the names of these flowers were; I was hoping that this one wasn't called by a name that would also describe me. Dealing with my impatience was enough for one day. I was curious, so I asked her, "What's that called? I love the purple and green combination."

"Persian Shield. They're one of my favorites. They always look good, no matter what I mix them with. Do you like them?"

"I love them. They even look like a shield." I couldn't help but reflect on the protection I was feeling after this morning's prayer. However, I couldn't say anything to Crystal, for she would think I had lost it if I told her that I had prayed with Mr. Mantis that morning. "Well, I better go downstairs and get back to work; I'll let you finish your watering."

I scurried to my office and realized I left my briefcase and laptop in the car, so I went back to retrieve them. As I got them out and was opening the side door, I heard the voice again, "Hi Neighbor, it's so good to see you back. How's the custom fixture business, Thomas?"

This time he was down below, next to the house, in the flowers below the fence to the left of the gate. "Much better, thanks."

"That's what I figured."

"Exactly, that's why I came back. You not only helped me today, but you knew my name. How's that?"

"How's what?" He cocked his head and I could swear he was wearing a smile.

"How did you know my name? I never told you. I just met you this morning."

"We may never have met formally, but I've been watching you for a while. I've heard Crystal, call you by name. I knew if I called you by name, I would get your attention. I did, didn't I?"

I laughed, "I'm not sure if a talking insect needs to call someone by name to get their attention, but yes, I guess it helped. It made me come back here this morning."

"I figured you would think about it. I have lots to share with you."

"Really, well I have more to ask you. But how did you get from the back amongst the Persian Shield to this side of the house in the time I ran back here?"

"I didn't."

My brow furrowed and eyeballs widened, "What do you mean, you didn't? Crystal and I both saw you out back."

"That wasn't me."

"That wasn't you. You mean it was another mantis?"

"Absolutely. You mean you couldn't tell the difference? Are you thinking that all mantis look alike?"

I thought he was messing with me, but I answered anyhow. "Of course, it's not like I talk to a praying mantis every day."

"Didn't the abdomen look quite a bit longer and fuller than mine? It was a female, my precious bride!"

"I didn't really notice. You're kidding me; you have a wife?"

"I call her 'my bride.' Isn't she lovely? Not a blemish on her. I'm preparing to meet with her soon." Just then he turned his head quickly and disappeared as Crystal was coming through the gate of the fence.

"Tom, what are you doing out here?" My wife had just left me on the porch a few minutes ago expecting me to be in my office, diligently at work.

"Aw, I just came to get my stuff out of the car, and I got distracted out here. I'm just noticing all these flowers that I never really noticed much before. You do an awesome job. Everything's truly beautiful, including you, my precious bride of 37 years."

Smiling and almost laughing, she raised one eyebrow, "You sure you're okay? Come on in the house, I'll help you get situated at your desk and make you a cup of coffee so you can get to work. You need to sell some light bulbs. Have you sold any light bulbs today?"

I laughed as she helped me into the house. I enjoyed her teasing me, my precious bride.

I NEED TO KNOW MORE

My workday went by quickly, and I got a lot accomplished. I sold lots of light bulbs and fixtures that day and set up some appointments for later in the week. Now if Crystal asked her usual question, I could enthusiastically say, "I did!"

As I was waiting for dinner, I was curious. I needed to look up some facts about the praying mantis and understand my friend a little better. Apparently, he understood me on many different levels. The least I could do was get to know him and his bride better.

As I went on the internet, I found several articles about the mantis species, but also found several videos about the stick-like creature. I started to watch but was interrupted by a tapping on my office window. I tried to ignore it, but it was an odd sound, so I paused the video and went to the window.

My mantis mentor was tapping on the outside of the windowsill, obviously trying to get my attention. I opened the office door and knelt outside beside the sill. "What's up, my friend" I was feeling a bit familiar with him by now.

"I need your help."

Now, I was really curious: "You need my help? How in the world can I help you?"

"Can you show me where you saw my bride? I can feel and smell her scent, but I haven't been able to find her. It's almost as though she's hiding from me."

"She was up on the back deck, you know, where I first found you. Do you want me to take you there? Hop on my palm and I'll take you?"

"No, I just wanted to be close to her. I like the journey; I don't want you to take me there before she's ready for me. On my way to find her, I have lots to do."

"Really, like what?"

"I need to consume as much nourishment as possible before I meet with her, then I'll give her all of my attention."

As I was enjoying this interesting repartee, I heard a voice from within the house, "Hey Honey, come to dinner. It's getting cold."

"You better get going, Tom. Don't keep her waiting. She's too important to do that."

"Well, we both keep each other waiting quite a bit. It's not every day that I talk to a praying mantis."

"Don't worry Tom, we'll talk again. It's not quite my time to leave yet," he remarked with a new tone that made me even more curious.

"What do you mean by that? When is it your time to leave?"

"Tom, go eat with your wife and daughter. I see a grasshopper on the Hardy Begonia over there. I need to sneak up on him if I'm going to have dinner also."

"Okay, but you promise we'll talk some more, right?"

"Absolutely."

As I was turning, I had a thought, then blurted out, "Hey, you know my name, but I don't know your name. How can I call out to you if I want to talk?"

"Oh, don't you worry, I'll find you."

"Come on, what's your name?"

"Okay, you can call me Sonny."

"Sonny? Really?"

"Well, it's a sort of nickname, or a form of a name I like to call myself."

"What do you like? I want to call you what you like to be called, just like I'd like to be called Tom, rather than Thomas or Tommy."

"My favorite name is a bit longer and has a little explanation behind it. But I don't have time right now—that grasshopper's busy eating and I want to be busy eating him."

"Okay, you can explain later, but before I go upstairs, what's your name?"

"Alright, I like to be known as the Son of Mantis. Now, no more questions."

With that, he leaped out to the Hardy Begonia and had captured his dinner. I was amazed at the speed and agility he possessed. I was shocked at how my gentle praying friend was feasting within seconds. I was becoming more curious than ever to learn more, but it was time to eat.

I turned off my computer and ran up the five steps from my office to the kitchen. On my way to the dinner table, I found myself thinking, *the Son of Mantis. Hmmmmm, Son of Mantis. Where have I heard that before?*

6

WHAT'S IN A NAME?

I was distracted during dinner, but I enjoyed the crunchy baked chicken my wife had prepared. I couldn't help but think of Sonny's dinner at the same time and laughed to myself. I didn't realize the laugh was discernible to my family.

My daughter, Faith, who we have always called Faithy or even Faify like one of my grandchildren had pronounced it, raised one eyebrow and questioned, "You haven't said a word, but you just laughed out loud; what's so funny?"

"Just thinking about how good dinner is tonight."

"And that's funny? I can't wait to hear how you react when you hear the dessert Mom made."

"What?"

My wife interjected, "Grasshopper pie."

I choked. I laughed. I coughed. My wife and daughter hovered around me ready to do the Heimlich maneuver. Finally, I caught my breath and took a drink of water.

"Dad, are you alright?"

"What was that all about," my wife was more curious than worried. "Tom, you sure are acting funny. Are you sure you're alright? You got up too early this morning, maybe you need to go to bed early and get a good night's rest."

"Not before I get some of that pie. I'm looking forward to the crunchy crunch of those grasshopper parts."

My wife and daughter rolled their eyes and shook their heads.

We enjoyed the remainder of our meal and the grasshopper pie, but it was still way too early to go to bed. So, while Faith and Mom were watching some YouTube shorts, I went into my bedroom and sat down in my recliner and picked up the Bible as I was still thinking of Sonny's name.

Then, I remembered that Jesus referred to himself quite often as the "Son of Man." I went to the back of my Bible to look that name up in the concordance.

The first reference I found was Mark 2:10 when Jesus said, "But that you may know that the Son of Man has authority on earth to forgive sin," and then in Mark 2:28, "Therefore the Son of Man is also Lord of the Sabbath."

Jesus referred to Himself as the Son of Man often in all four gospels. I never noticed that before, but obviously it must be important, or He would not have continually used this term.

Sonny was identifying with Jesus Christ. This praying insect wasn't content with just praying, he wanted those around him to understand something more. I needed that something.

Over the last few years, my family had experienced some life-changing trauma, and work had been extremely stressful for me. Somewhere in between, I got lost in the shuffle. My identity and God's identity in me were clouded. Sonny's appearance was forcing me to re-focus.

I kept reading to discover who Jesus said He was. I spent the evening reading and praying, asking God to show me more about this new revelation. I couldn't wait to see Sonny again, or more accurately, "The Son of Mantis."

I entered into a time of worship, giving thanks for my renewed devotion. Time had gotten away from me, and before I knew it, I had been immersed in prayer for almost two hours.

I sang the old hymn, *What a Friend We Have in Jesus*, which I hadn't sung in decades, but suddenly, it was real to me. My prayers were genuine, my faith seemed divine; I was truly a friend of the Son of Man.

7

"GO! IT'S TIME"

I ran off to work the next morning with a song in my heart and a prayer on my lips, "God don't let me forget what You're teaching me." I went into the office to find that the custom fixture project was being re-worked by the manufacturer and it would be out the door in a couple of days. Everything was running smoothly and on time. I could focus on my other work and take care of my local customers.

I got a call from one of my favorites, Wesley, who was the building engineer for more than ten different properties. I loved working with Wes because he always knew what he was looking for. He would do his research beforehand, and I didn't have to guess what he needed. I was able to take his information and get him a good deal. Today, Wes needed a quote to change all the lighting fixtures in two parking garages. I went to a few different vendors to see what was best for the application and before the end of the day, I sent Wes a very competitive quote.

I had gotten several requests for quotes and product information from other customers and the day was speeding along. I was looking forward to going home so I could find my friend, looking forward to sharing my newfound revelation of Scripture. Sonny was discipling me. Who would or could have guessed?

Before I put away my laptop and briefcase, I got a call from Wes asking how soon he could get the fixtures. I was elated for he already had the approval but just needed a timeframe. Today began the second week in September, and he wanted to get them installed by the 19th, since he was going on vacation on the 20th and wanted to supervise the project.

I put an order in our system, then called the manufacturer to get an ETA. They were in stock, so everything was working out. I called Wes and informed him that he would get them in less than a week and he could schedule a crew so that everything could be done by the 19th.

I was ending my day with a $40,000 fixture order. What a day! As I packed up my laptop and got all my stuff together in my briefcase, I looked up at the calendar: September 19. Suddenly, that date hit me like a ton of bricks!

Two years ago, early in the morning on September 19, I was in Pittsburgh, Pennsylvania in St. Margaret's Hospital at the bedside of my oldest daughter, Heather, aged 43, who had just passed away. Suddenly my day was interrupted by a flood of emotion.

As I drove home, my mind revisited some intense memories. I pulled up to the side of the house, got out of the van and started to enter the side door. Then I heard that voice, "Hey Tom, down here. Come sit down."

I looked to my left and Sonny was on top of the gas meter. Crystal had left a folding chair at the side of the house.

"Come sit down, you look like you need a friend."

"Sonny, what are you doing on the gas meter?"

"Waiting for you; I wanted to continue our conversation from yesterday, but that can wait."

"I had a great day in sales, but it was ruined when I realized that the day I need to deliver a large order is the anniversary of my oldest daughter's death two years ago."

"I'm a good listener, Tom."

"There's a lot to listen to."

"Take your time."

I was on the back porch and saw Crystal and Faith just starting dinner. It will be quite a while before it's time to come in."

I unfolded the chair, sat down, and began. "I was remembering the week before Heather passed: Crystal and I had driven up to Pittsburgh to help Heather move out of her rundown, tenement-like apartment and find something new. Her landlord was evicting her because she hadn't paid rent for several months, and more importantly, her friend, Terry, had called and notified us that Heather was very sick.

"Before hearing from Terry, Heather had explained how she had twice discharged herself from the hospital in two months after admitting herself with severe swelling in her legs. She told us it was because of issues concerning a gastric bypass operation from 18 years earlier. We didn't quite understand, but we trusted that Heather had a handle on it. She downplayed it quite a bit, so we let it go.

"However, upon seeing her, we sensed it was more serious than she described. We took her to a favorite Chinese restaurant and observed our daughter, who was usually vibrant and expressive, talk very slowly and at times seem a little confused. We weren't sure what to think. After a couple of hours at the restaurant, we took her home, but we were staying at Terry's, who had plenty of room for us.

"As we drove the 15 minutes to Terry's, we discussed several things: Heather's unusual behavior, her need to move out of the slum, and all the work necessary to perform the move. We had driven thirteen hours that day, and knew we had several days of hard work ahead of us so we turned in early because we were very tired.

"The next morning came too quickly, and we had no time to think about yesterday's questions. Heather had just gotten a new job, so first we took her to work. Then we walked into her apartment: I was shocked: 'Crystal, look at this place, did a hurricane come through here?'

"Heather was always a clean freak, much like my wife, always vacuuming, always tidying. So, when we came in, greeted by her rambunctious Boston terrier, Mac, and saw everything in disarray, we were shocked. It appeared as if nothing had been touched in months, but there was no time to analyze. We had too much to do.

"The more we cleaned and packed, the more clues were revealed about Heather's current state. We knew she had been battling with alcohol but had no clue to what extent. Recently Crystal had challenged her, and Heather swore that she had stopped drinking, but obviously the damage was already done; not only physically, but also in other ways.

"Just two months prior she had been fired from her job where she had worked for more than 13 years. What's more, her Aunts Susan and Nancy, my sisters, had done the firing. This was a tough one, but they felt like they had no recourse but to end her employment. She had repeatedly caused issues at work that would have caused termination, but she was given a lot of leeway because she was kin. I know they thought they could help Heather, but her slack turned to frustration and their frustration came to a head.

"Heather's 19-year-old daughter, Marina, had moved out to live with her dad and attend college in Tennessee a little before the firing incident. A little after that, Heather's car was repossessed. Every aspect of Heather's life seemed to be crashing around her. Weeks before we came down, I had a conversation with her that was quite disheartening, as she confessed her depressed state and lack of hope. I tried to encourage her and would sometimes pray, but her heart had grown cold toward the God she had known as a child and teenager. Divorce, disappointments, unforgiveness, and regrets had eaten her up inside and it was taking its toll. She didn't want to hear about God.

"During the next few days, we were consumed with packing, trashing, and moving furniture. Heather would go to work doing manicures and pedicures, and we would go to work at her apartment. At the same time, we pursued several leads for a new place that my sisters had suggested. Fortunately, we were getting help from my brothers-in-law and nephews who lived close by. We were able to move Heather's furniture into my brother-in-law Umberto's warehouse and business run by my nephew, Damian. Then, my brother-in-law, Paul, and nephew, Matt, helped us pack and move. Without this assistance, it would've been more grueling than it was; and it was grueling! Along with all that, we had to find a home for Mac. With much prayer and God's guidance, we found a rescue that took him and placed him in a good home.

"Getting rid of Mac was a big deal for Heather, but she knew the chance of finding a new place with a dog was slim, so with much prodding and after many tears, she allowed it. Then came more disappointment: An apartment we found the day after we arrived fell through, and we were forced to investigate other less desirable choices.

"By then it was Sunday the 16th and it was Heather's first day off since we arrived. It was the first chance we had to spend a good block of time with her. As the day wore on, it was obvious that Heather was not well. When my brother-in-law Paul arrived to help, he strongly suggested that we take her to the hospital — even if she refused.

"That evening, we all went over to Terry's for dinner. We knew that Terry and her husband, Tony, would support us in our pleading with Heather to go to the hospital. Terry had been a great friend to Heather and her initial phone call helped us decide to drop everything to travel north.

As we drove from Heather's to Terry's, we first suggested the hospital. Heather was adamant and started crying that she did not want to go, but we emphatically poured out our concern and she softened. Even with the apprehension, we had a very pleasant dinner and a lot of good conversation, but as we finished, we told Terry of our talk in the car. Terry stood up and came over to Heather and embraced her. She cried as Heather cried, and we had an agreement to visit the hospital. We were on our way. Crystal and I had been praying a lot over the previous five days, and we could sense God leading us to this moment.

"It's important to mention the one thing that had occurred before we embarked for Pittsburgh that had the biggest impact. The day before Terry called us, we had traveled to a Christian gathering with several people from my church. It was a 75-minute drive north of where we lived. We were in a Christian bookstore where a woman had been praying with individuals for several hours. As the store was closing, I felt impressed to approach the woman and introduce myself. She told me that her name was Eileen, which just happens to be Heather's middle name. I then asked Eileen, "Do you have a word for me? Do you have something for me from God?"

"Eileen paused, looking at me, took my hands, and closed her eyes, 'Yes; there's an open door, before it wasn't open, but now it is. Go, it's time.'

"Well, at that moment, I didn't know what any of that meant, but when Terry called us the next day, we knew exactly what it meant. When I told my youngest daughter, Faith, she said, "Dad, I think your daughter needs you." I agreed, and we were off. The next day, we packed. I borrowed money from a friend knowing I could use it to help Heather, and the day after that we left early for the 13-hour drive to Pittsburgh.

"Now we were driving to St. Margaret's Hospital where Heather had signed herself out twice in the last six weeks. We were believing they would find out what was wrong with Heather, and she would have to stay in as long as was necessary to get straightened out. We had moved her out of the slumlord tenement where she had lived for more than a dozen years, and we would find her the perfect place to live while we encouraged her recovery. We believed this would all work out. In less than 20 minutes, we were in the hospital ER waiting for the doctor.

"As I looked at our daughter laying on a hospital gurney, I was hopeful. The doctor came in, did a thorough examination, and looked at her charts. He immediately scheduled some tests and then looked back and forth from Heather to us. 'Heather, you have been in here a few times lately. And I see that you discharged yourself when we wanted to keep you. You're a very sick woman: we've scheduled some tests and will admit you now. We'll know more tomorrow.'

"It was after 10:00 p.m. and we were all tired. We gave Heather a kiss and prayed that all would be revealed and treated properly. Crystal and I drove back to Terry's believing that the next day would bring healing for Heather and some new leads for an apartment."

8

"GOD,
I LOOK TO YOU"

I paused, realizing that Sonny was listening intently, "Are you sure you want to hear all this?"

"Of course, Tom. So when you left her at the hospital, you felt she'd finally get the care she needed. Go on."

"I was sleeping soundly the next morning when I heard my phone buzzing. It was 7:00 a.m. and I saw that it was from St. Margaret's. I rushed to answer as I tried to awaken. 'Mr. Borga, this is Heather's doctor. I need you to come in and talk. Heather is in ICU and we need to discuss some options. When can you come in?'

"My blood ran cold as I tried to process the information. ICU? We were just having tests done, right? We would figure out what was wrong and prescribe a treatment, right? I couldn't quite grasp the whole ICU idea. Suddenly, I was filled with fear as a deep chill ran down my spine. I found out when we needed to be there and hung up.

"I explained all to Crystal, and we rushed to get ready. As we were leaving for the hospital, one of our tires went flat: sometimes, things happen in a series that point in a certain direction. The direction I was feeling wasn't good, I was really scared but had to hold it all together. I called several places in the area where I could get a new tire or one patched. AAA came to change our flat while Crystal and I were like robots, not saying much, just doing what we needed to do to get this done.

When we finally got to the hospital, it took us a while to find Heather's room where they were putting in some IVs and preparing her for something, but we weren't sure what. The nurse took us to her doctor, a very young-looking woman with a very compassionate face. She took us into another room and sat us down.

She began, 'Mr. and Mrs. Borga, as we performed a CAT scan and several other tests, we discovered some things that are very serious. Heather's kidneys are in bad shape, and that's why she's had the swelling for the last several months, but since she was here last, there has been a new development. Her liver is also in bad shape, and her blood isn't good. We feel like we need to do a transfusion, but Heather can't communicate with us, and we would like your permission. Or, if there's a closer relative, we need to talk to them.'

Much had changed since last night and it was hard to believe that Heather couldn't communicate. Her daughter was the closest relative so we would have to call her. Marina had no idea what was going on. We knew this wasn't going to be easy.

"'Her 19-year-old daughter is in Tennessee going to college and living with her father. We'll have to get a hold of her. Do you think we should ask her to come?'

"The doctor was candid: 'Yes, her daughter needs to be here, we aren't sure which way this will go.'

"We had a heart-to-heart talk with the doctor before calling Marina. We were now aware of Heather's dire physical state but realized that Heather was in God's hands. We asked the doctor if she would pray with us, and she did.

"With a heavy heart, we called Marina. At first, we couldn't get a hold of her, but after leaving some messages, she returned the call. Marina was devastated, but we told her to call the doctor as soon as possible and to come as soon as she could. She did both, and we planned to pick her up at the airport the next morning with her stepmom, Holly, who has always been a source of encouragement for Marina.

"That day was filled with one emotional scene after another. We called everyone close to Heather about the situation. Her younger sisters — Faith in Georgia, aged 21 at the time; her 35-years-old twin sisters, Alicia in North Carolina and Amber in Florida; and older sister Christina living near Seattle, Washington. They were all dumbfounded when we told them the latest developments. They began trying to figure out if and when they could get there.

"Her Aunt Susan and Nancy weren't in town that week; they had gone to Palm Springs to meet our younger sister, Janice, for a week away. They would have come back, but couldn't get flights out for several days, so I told them to wait and see. I spoke to her friends and relatives close by and many rushed to the hospital. Heather could see and sense the people around her but couldn't speak. We weren't sure what she was hearing or understanding, but we had many of her loved ones, including her sisters and Aunts call, and we held a phone up to Heather's ear as they talked. Heather responded as best she could as I could see some recognition and forgiveness flow back and forth.

"At one point, three of her cousins who lived in town, her two uncles, and some friends stood in a circle and prayed for her around her bed. The circumstances were bringing people together to rally for our daughter, many of whom Heather had alienated over the years. The love they felt for Heather was expressed quite genuinely as we all prayed earnestly for her life.

"That evening when Crystal was in the waiting room, I sang worship songs and prayed in Heather's ICU room. I talked to Heather about many things and expressed how much God loved her. I felt a peace in the room; I didn't sense the presence of death. As a child, she had expressed a love for Jesus, and as a teen, she was baptized. I had seen desire in her at times to mature spiritually, but I wasn't sure where she was with the Lord at this time. She had given place to some other philosophies in conflict with faith, and I was concerned that she would die without Jesus. As I leaned in, pleading with her to respond to God, she opened her mouth and said, 'I know, Dad, I know.'

"She couldn't keep her eyes open as she went in and out of consciousness. I wanted to know more. What did she know? Was she brushing me aside like so many times when I was telling her something she didn't want to hear? 'I know Dad, I know'! Or was she responding to my heart's cry for her to respond to God with a sincere, 'I know Dad, I know.'

"We had been through so much with Heather over the years. Heather was adopted at age ten after having lived with us for a year before that. Technically, she came into our lives as our niece, the daughter of Crystal's brother, Joe, and his wife, Pat, before they were divorced. She ended up living at Crystal's grandparents' home in North Hollywood, California, the same town in which Crystal and I were married just a year before Heather came to live with us.

"We thought Heather's stay was temporary, but after discovering that neither parent wanted her, I heard God speak quietly to my heart, 'Raise her as your own.' And after several months, it was confirmed as both birth parents consented for us to adopt her.

"I remember that day very clearly. We met a sweet Judge at the Burbank Courthouse who completed all the documents but found a mistake on one. He finalized the adoption but told me that the mistake needed to be corrected and paperwork brought back before it could be filed for us to get the new birth certificate. So after getting home, I corrected the document and flew back to the courthouse before it closed. I brought back a cake and gift for Heather's adoption day — a toy stuffed penguin. "Pengy" became a favorite of hers that she still owned. We brought it to the hospital.

"Growing up, Heather was a handful and always challenged us, but God used Heather being in our lives in a myriad of ways. When she was 15, her older half-sister, Christina, who was an adult and estranged from Heather for years, reached out to her. Because of this, Christina became close to us and as she came to know the love of Christ, she began looking for her other half sisters, Amber and Alicia, who were in a foster home. Eventually, they were found only a half block away from the church we were attending.

"So one Sunday, after years of separation, all four sisters were meeting for the first time. From that day forward, we forged a close bond with Christina, and it led to us adopting the twins about a year later. Because of Heather's initial adoption, our family became much larger, adding the twins and Christina. Faith, being our only birth child, came several years later, born when Heather was already out of the house and living in Pittsburgh, having graduated from Pittsburgh Beauty Academy and about to be married to Marina's Dad, Chris, who was in the Navy.

"That was another chapter in Heather's life. The Navy had taken them to Jacksonville, China Lake, CA, and Seattle. Heather and Chris divorced when Marina was six after which Heather moved back to Pittsburgh and was hired by my sisters to work at their beauty salon.

"When she was a child, we had fun with Heather's name and would say, 'Heather the feather in any kind of weather.' Like a feather, she seemed to float above the wind and could weather every storm. However, Heather was in a storm now that wasn't so easy to float through. This storm was taking her life, and I was helpless. My precious child that I 'raised as my own' was dying.

"The next day was full. We picked up Marina and Holly early at the airport and went directly to the hospital. We left Marina alone as she cried at her mother's side. She talked and talked, and I could see Heather responding as best she could to her daughter's tenderness.

"The doctor came to us and asked us what to do if Heather should pass. Should they try to bring her back? Marina had given permission for us to make that decision, for she wasn't in a place to do so. Honestly, at this point, this wasn't easy for us either. We prayed and felt like we had dedicated our child to God from the moment she entered our home; it was no different now. We signed a paper: If she passed away, they would not use any artificial means to keep her alive.

"During that day we had to make other decisions concerning her treatment amidst the phone calls and visits from those who loved Heather. Our daughter, Faith, had finally secured a flight but wouldn't arrive until after midnight. I had many people from my home church and work friends praying for Heather. In fact, I had people all over the country praying.

"I was trying to hear from God as to what He had for our daughter, but I must say I was numb and couldn't sense much of anything. This whole situation was the last thing from our thoughts less than a week before. But God knew. This didn't take Him by surprise. And He knew that we needed to be there. He made sure that Eileen and Terry got us here, and I couldn't help but be more grateful.

"Marina was at the hospital at her Mom's side with her stepmother, Holly. The funny thing is that Holly and Heather got along, they may not have been best buddies, but there was no animosity there. It was good that Holly was there with Marina.

"After midnight, we arrived at the airport to pick up our daughter Faith. We learned that Faith's plane had arrived and it was a little after 1:20 a.m. on Wednesday morning, September 19 that we got a call while we were waiting for Faith. It was Holly. Heather had passed.

"As we went to the arrivals escalator to meet our youngest, we knew what our first words would be. Crystal and I embraced Faith, 'Your sister is gone. Heather just passed.' We three embraced and cried. We all needed to cry, and we needed to cry big time!

"Minutes later we were on our way back to the hospital to say one last goodbye to Heather. When we got into the room and hugged Marina and Holly, everything was so quiet and Heather's body had not been touched. The nurses had taken away all the machines that were monitoring her vitals and she laid there peacefully. I couldn't help but notice there was no stress on her face, something that I hadn't seen in years.

"We said our goodbyes Crystal, Faith, and I, together and individually. Marina and Holly had already said their piece. I don't remember what I said, but I was okay. God had shown himself to be faithful: He brought us to be with my daughter during the last week of her life. What a gift, for Heather and for all of us. Because we were there, my daughter, who was more ill than any of us knew, spent her last days with family and friends who loved her. The communication wasn't as fluid as we wanted, but we all got to express our love to her.

"The next days weren't easy: Making funeral arrangements and planning Heather's memorial, getting everyone into Pittsburgh from all over the country: Heather's sisters, aunts, uncles and cousins, other relatives, and friends. But it was worth it, for that Sunday, September 23, we had a beautiful service in the back patio area of my sister Susan's home. That is the same place Heather's wedding to Marina's dad took place more than 20 years earlier.

"We memorialized Heather's life and came to recognize that no matter how turbulent, every life is worth celebrating and every life has immense worth. Heather's death brought unity to our whole family that hadn't been there in a long time. As we talked and cried, prayed and laughed we saw the great blessings in Heather's life and her death."

I looked closely at Sonny, and if I didn't know better, I'd think he had a tear in his eye. And then one more memory came rushing in, "You know Sonny, we began Heather's memorial with a song, and we ended it with the same song." I began to sing:

God, I look to You, I won't be overwhelmed. Give me vision to see things like you do.

God, I look to You, You're where my help comes from. Give me wisdom, You know just what to do.

I will love You, Lord my Strength, I will love You, Lord my Shield, I will love you, Lord my Rock, forever.

All my days, I will love You, God.
(©Bethel Music Publishing, used by permission)

I sat in the driveway with my new friend, able to look back and see how the Son of Man showed up in this man's life in a very special way when he and his family needed it most. As I sat there crying and singing, Sonny joined me in a chorus, "God, I look to You . . ."

FOOD FOR THOUGHT

I heard Crystal in the garage, so I knew she'd be looking for me. Sonny hopped down from the gas meter as he moved toward the backyard. I entered the garage and gave my wife a peck on the cheek as we went up-stairs for dinner.

Crystal taunted me with her usual question, "Did you sell any light bulbs today?" I told her about the big order and about what it brought up in my heart. Both my wife and Faith reached out and placed their hands on mine. Dinner was a good time to talk, so that's what we did. We ate and talked about Heather. We laughed and reminisced about our oldest, as Faith, our youngest, asked to tell stories that we hadn't talked about since Heather passed.

I chuckled as I told of the day that we brought Heather home to live with us. She was living with Crystal's grandparents and they were beside themselves.

They were in their late seventies and Heather was the most rambunctious nine-year-old one could imagine. I went to their home by myself to pick her up, only to find that she wasn't there. Grandma excitedly explained that Heather was at the neighbor's home; she had run out of the house right into the neighbor's front door and wouldn't come out.

I calmed Grandma and went next door. The neighbor let me in and just pointed to the couch. I looked behind it, and there was Heather crouched like a scared animal refusing to go back to Grandma's. I told her that she didn't need to fear because I would take her home to our house. She liked Aunt Crystal and me. I put her in the car, then went in to talk with Grandma and Grandpa. They were precious people who had a heart to care for Heather, but it was not a good fit. I told them we would keep her until we figured out what to do next. The rest is history.

We sat in the kitchen for a couple hours. We hadn't spent this much time talking in quite a while. The emotions of the day turned to stories of gratitude and fond memories. We finished dinner and I said I would do the dishes. Crystal and Faith went upstairs as I slowly washed and dried the dishes and cleaned up the cooking mess.

I went outside in the back to sit on the deck and enjoy the evening air. It was finally a little cooler that day and by then it was about 75 degrees. I loved to sit out there until a hummingbird would come and buzz by my head to the feeder that was in front of my dining room window. I waited awhile to see if one would arrive, but none came.

As I got up to go in the house, there was Sonny on our favorite New Guinea Impatiens, seeming to just watch me. I looked down at him, "And what are you looking at, Mr. Son of Mantis?"

"Someone who has had quite a day. Thank you for sharing with me earlier, Tom. I'm learning a lot about you."

"I'm learning a lot about you, too. You made me think about your name last night, and I spent a lot of time reading the Bible and worshiping. It prepared me for what I experienced today. Thanks for listening to me."

"I'm all ears. That's an expression of course because I'm an insect and I really don't have any ears. But I bet you would love to know more about me. Here's some food for thought: I could see you in the kitchen doing the dishes and trying to scrub that one pan with baked-on slime. I have very keen eyesight, you know. That's one of the things you will find out about me if you do a little more research. Just some food for thought"

"How did you know I was doing some research on you?"

"The other evening when I tapped on your downstairs window, I saw you doing some research about my kind. You didn't get very far, did you?"

"No, you interrupted before I could watch a video about the praying mantis."

"Well, why watch a video when you can ask the real thing?"

"You've got a point there, but I'm not sure what to ask."

Just then the door opened wide and Crystal came out, "Hey, Husband, come in and spend time with your wife. I want to hear more about this big sale, and we can cuddle.

All of that sounded appealing, but I wanted to finish my conversation with Sonny. He had really piqued my curiosity. As I turned my head, Sonny disappeared, and I was tempted to say "Cuddling sounds great, Crystal, but I'm having a conversation with the Son of Mantis. Could this wait a few minutes?"

But instead, I said, "Alright dear, I was just getting some fresh air and hoping to experience a hummingbird, but I guess I'm ready to come in."

As I walked in, I heard a hummingbird zoom past me, then suddenly, silence. I looked around and saw Sonny on the other side of the deck with the bird trapped in his razor arms with Sonny munching on his head. I gasped, but didn't say a word.

Crystal loved those hummingbirds but talk about "food for thought." Yes, it was definitely time to go in. I was ready for a good cuddle.

MORE RESEARCH

I woke up early the next day to spend some time with the Lord and seek Him for my daily bread. I had a newfound desire to get up early and pray. As I went to sleep each night, I began to anticipate my time with Him in the morning.

After about an hour, I found myself thinking about Sonny, wanting to do a little research about my mantis friend. This time, it was still early. In fact, it was still dark, so I figured no one in my family or Sonny would interrupt.

As I entered the words "praying mantis" in my search engine, I found the same videos about their behavior I had been watching when Sonny interrupted me. However, I decided to read a few written articles before watching.

I came to one article that listed the various attributes of this amazing insect. It revealed some facts I had already witnessed which the Son of Mantis had proudly mentioned: They have amazing eyesight. Seeing 3-D like humans, but even better, their eyes are made up of thousands of smaller eyes and they have eyes in between their two bulging eyes. Those extra eyes cannot be seen by us, but they are utilized quite effectively. Their eyesight, quick reflexes, and hunting abilities were highlighted in the article.

A mantis can spring forth to capture their prey twice as fast as we can blink our eyes; no wonder that grasshopper never had a chance. Often, they will consume creatures much bigger than they are. I found out that the hummingbird is one of their favorite meals. I'm not sure if Crystal would appreciate that fact, but to see it with my own eyes was incredible.

Camouflaged in their environment, the species normally resembles the plants and flowers where they live, making it much easier to surprise their prey. It is imperative they become skilled hunters since they only eat live, moving food and have insatiable appetites. Often, they eat the brains first. Maybe that is why my friend is so smart!

My sense of awe for this tiny creature increased with each sentence. But then, I was flabbergasted as the next few lines threw me for a loop:

> "One of the most popular praying mantis facts is the penchant for cannibalism in many species. Females of some praying mantis species will actually eat the male when mating with him. After the male performs a complex mating dance, the female will bite the head or legs off the male during the mating act" (Ehrlich Debugged – *The Pest Control Blog*)

I was stunned. I had heard something like that before, but I was not thinking in those terms. This was my friend, the Son of Mantis. They were referring to some other mantis, right, not Sonny, who so wonderfully engages me to think more of my Creator and dig deep into my Bible? This had to be a mistake or didn't apply to Sonny's species. I continued to read:

"However, in the wild, it is said that this occurs less than 30% of the time."

Whew, that means Sonny has a 70% chance of not being devoured by his bride. That made me feel a little better, but I still felt uneasy. My friendship would sooner or later come to an end. After all, he is an insect, and they probably don't live long. Even so, that is not the way I would want it to end. I was determined to talk it over with Sonny. Maybe I could help him come up with a strategy to avoid such a fate.

The sun was coming up and I had some appointments scheduled, but I needed to go out and find my friend. This needed to be discussed. I looked everywhere — on the deck, front porch, side gates, yard, bushes, even in the flowers around our mailbox. There was no sign of the Son of Mantis. I called out his name, both names, and looked under every leaf I could touch.

Could he and his bride have left the area already? No, it was coming close to the time of the year when they would be mating. Oh no, is that what happened between last night and this morning? I was worried for Sonny, but I was late for an appointment. I had no choice but to get ready for work and take off.

I said a little prayer for my friend, "Dear Lord, a week ago, I would have thought someone who experienced what I'm experiencing would be a bit crazy. Maybe

I am crazy, but Sonny has been a real friend, and I need to see him. Would You protect him, and if he's still around, have him and I meet soon, so we can discuss what I've learned today? Amen."

I got in my car and stared in the rear-view mirror, hoping to somehow see him as I sped down the street. There was no sign of Sonny, only a stop sign, and I totally missed it. I was lucky there were no cars going the opposite way. However, there was one parked 30 feet in front of me on the opposite side of the street. It was a police car; I may not have seen the stop sign, but the parked officer saw me.

The next several minutes I tried to wrap my mind around why a policeman was in my quiet neighborhood handing out tickets to unsuspecting citizens. Of course, I did go through the stop sign, and I did violate the law, so I humbly accepted the ticket. I wanted to say something like, "But officer, I was distraught with emotion and concern over one of my best friends, which is why I went through the stop sign."

"So, tell me about your friend. What would cause you to totally ignore a stop sign, not even slow down?"

"My friend may have been cannibalized by his new bride this morning. Can you understand my concern?"

I guess I couldn't say any of that. So, I just went off to my first appointment, hoping that I could focus on my work as I wondered about my good friend's fate.

"THAT WASN'T ME"

Work was frustrating that day. Traffic was horrific. I was traveling all the way to the other side of Atlanta into Gwinnett County, normally a 40-minute drive — today it was an hour and a half. Upon visiting my first customer, I found out that some samples I sent did not show up. We ended up trying the one sample he did receive and found out that one of his buildings had several different but similar types of bulbs in the sockets. It was good to find this out, but it would have been much easier if the other samples had arrived.

I went on to my next customer who was supposed to meet me for lunch, only to find out that he couldn't make it. Then I visited another close-by customer who also wasn't available. I ventured over to a fourth at a private high school that had a problem with one of their emergency fixtures.

We got on a ladder and took pictures of the different

part numbers on the emergency ballast, a part number I had never seen in my 38 years of sales. When I got down from the ladder, I called the manufacturer only to find that the product was no longer made and had no replacement. I also found there was no emergency ballast in the market that listed the light bulb combination of that fixture. I told the customer I would do more research and get back to him.

I left the area before 2:30 p.m., making sure I got out of Atlanta before traffic began to build. However, there was road construction on the other side and some "Looky-loos" caused a fender bender that stopped all traffic. I didn't get back to the office until 4:30 p.m., just in time to make sure my warehouse had sent out some new samples to my first customer. I was worn out but had accomplished very little; I was glad to be going home.

I left my laptop and briefcase in the office. I decided I would come back early the next day to catch up on some of the day's activity. Halfway home, I got a terrible picture in my head of Sonny running for his life, trying to escape from a half-crazed but hungry female mantis. As I pulled in the driveway, I looked up at the fence.

There he was!

Sonny was alive and well and waiting for my arrival back home. I bent down, picked up the ticket I had received that morning, and waved it at Sonny as I exited the vehicle, "Hey Neighbor, you cost me $175.00 today, you Son of a Mantis. I'm so glad to see you!"

"I'm glad to see you too, Tom. But how could I cost you $175.00? You know, many people think praying mantises bring good fortune."

"I was worried about you this morning, I looked everywhere! In the back, in the front, on the sides, in the bushes, the plants, the fence, everywhere! Where were you?"

"I was right here, on the side of the house. If you haven't noticed, I kind of blend in with the shrubbery. I saw you race off and go through the stop sign, and I saw the very nice officer put out his hand to stop you and write you a nice note. I suppose that nice note cost you $175.00?"

"Exactly."

"I'm sorry, Tom, if you had slowed down a bit, you may have seen me. I'm so sorry about the $175.00 but look at it this way: How else can the city afford to get new street lighting? And if you're smart, you'll go down to the city operations office and see if you can sell them." I couldn't help but laugh, and Sonny laughed with me. Then he got excited and blurted out, "Can you sense her?"

"Sense who? What are you talking about?"

"My bride, her scent is in the air. It's getting close, our time is near. That's why I need to consume as much nourishment as possible, for my bride, my precious bride."

Just then, Sonny leaped across the driveway to a bush on the other side. He grabbed a tree frog that was also camouflaged and within seconds was devouring frog brains.

"Sonny, it's a good thing Crystal isn't watching you consume all her backyard delights. She loves those little tree frogs, and if she ever saw you eat another humming-bird, like last night, I think she would consider exiling you to wherever you came from."

"Hummingbird? You think I captured that hum-mingbird? I wish. That wasn't me. That was my bride. I also watched from the other side of the deck, and I was amazed as you were at her grace and skill. To capture that beautiful bird in midflight was truly a thing of beauty, but then she disappeared. Oh, my bride, she's so special! I can't wait to meet her!"

"What are you talking about, my precious bride? Are you crazy? Do you know what that bride can do to you?"

"Yes, I'm crazy in love with my bride and I long for our meeting. She's so important to me and means so much to me, I've been waiting so long. I'm consumed by thoughts of her!"

"Exactly, you're consumed, and you're going to be consumed! Your bride might very well consume you, eat you, digest you. Do you remember that hummingbird? That could be you!"

The Son of Mantis paused, swallowed hard, finishing a portion of the tree frog, then dropped the remains to the ground. Then he closed his eyes, and embraced himself with those prayer-like arms, "Oh, I certainly hope so, that's my dream. To be consumed by my bride means that I've fulfilled my purpose. That's why I was born. The end of me is the beginning for my bride to bear many offspring. She isn't complete unless she's fully nourished by the Son of Mantis, consuming him completely so that she may fulfill her purpose."

"But Sonny, you can't, you can't leave me, I've just begun to understand some things."

"Tom, everything you're understanding is straight from God. He's just using me to remind you of what He placed in you a long time ago, including the curiosity to finish your research."

"Well, I wished I'd never finished my research, then you would just disappear one day, and I wouldn't have thought much of it. Now, I'm going to picture you in place of that hummingbird."

"Now wait a second, think about everything you've just heard."

"Yes, I'm thinking that my good friend's going to be cannibalized!"

"Unless you eat my flesh and drink my blood, you can have no part in me, that is what Jesus said to His disciples. Do you think they thought He was crazy?"

"Yes, they must have thought that. How could they understand what that meant? "

"And many stopped following Him, except for his best friends who really knew Him. They may not have known what He meant, but they trusted Him. And later, during the Last Supper, He instituted communion at the Passover. Ultimately, they saw the big picture after His sacrifice, and now every Christian denomination celebrates and remembers our Lord through communion. Jesus meant for His disciples to consume Him."

"Wow, Sonny, I need to think on this for a while? There's a lot to digest here. Please, forgive the pun."

He gave me a wink and dropped to the ground to finish his frog. I paused, taking a long look at Sonny and thinking, "This may be the last time I see him."

12

GOD IS GOOD

As I entered the house, Crystal came flying out, "What are you doing, Tom? We're late; it's Tuesday. We told Bubby we would visit tonight."

I forgot about our visit to Bubby. I didn't feel like going out again, but I couldn't explain everything to Crystal, so I got back in the car and we drove. Bubby was about 40 minutes east of us, but I was in no hurry, making sure that I stopped completely at each stop sign and obeyed every traffic law.

Bubby was a dear 93-year-old Jewish woman who was the mother-in-law of one of the owners of my company. A few years ago, I was praying and journaling on a July Fourth holiday when I felt God prompting Crystal and I to start visiting Bubby. We had been visiting the local assisted living facility near our house, and we enjoyed spending time with the residents. We talked to them about Jesus and prayed with them. Bubby was an old

Jewish woman who equated Jesus with the Holocaust and did not want to hear the mention of His name.

When we first started visiting Bubby, we thought God would have us lead her to Christ, and after a visit or two, this stubborn old woman would become a Christian — and our job would be done! However, we needed to learn that love is patient, love is kind, and love does not seek its own agenda. Nearly three years later, we were still faithfully visiting her, and she had become our dear friend. We loved her and she loved us, but she still did not desire or comprehend the need to know Jesus as her Messiah.

Nonetheless, we had seen progress. During the past year, I had been studying an overview of the Bible, spending an enormous amount of time in the Old Testament and the history of the Jews. God had me reviewing almost every book of the Old Testament with Bubby and praying for her during every visit. After a while, she would allow Crystal and I to pray in the name of Yeshua, the Hebrew equivalent of Jesus.

One time, we were discussing Abram who would become father Abraham, the patriarch of the Jews. We showed Bubby in Genesis 12 that God promised to bless Abraham so that he and his descendants would bless all the families of the world. We explained to Bubby how God very purposely blessed Isaac, Jacob, his twelve sons, and then led Israel through King David and his lineage. Then eventually, despite Israel's rebellion, that lineage led us to Jesus of Nazareth, who eventually was the ultimate blessing of God to the world. She was enamored with this description and at one point blurted out, "You should come to the synagogue and tell this to our rabbi."

I knew that some things were sinking in, but somehow before the day was done, she would go off on some rabbit trail questioning God's goodness and the state of the world, ultimately leading to the unfairness of tragic events in her life.

As we walked in to visit Bubby, she smiled and kissed us. She was always happy to see us, and she had quite a sharp wit about her. She often would take us to dinner and was very generous. She had a big heart, but a wounded one; she had a difficult time letting go of hurtful issues. And if she believed something was true, forget it. She did not just accept anything anyone said without expressing her opinion, especially if her experience clashed with your opinion.

Today as we reviewed the goodness of God, she posed a question that I had heard many times, but never thought how it might be answered. Bubby very confidently exclaimed, "If God is so good, then how could He let Hitler come into power so quickly and do all the evil he did, including the killing of so many Jews?"

"Good question, Bubby. Why don't you ask God and see if He will answer you? He encourages us in Jeremiah that if we seek Him with all our heart, we'll surely find him."

"He won't answer me. You ask and tell me what He says."

I paused and thought this over. Will God answer such a question for me? I thought, "Yes, God loves to answer the heart cry of His people. I believe He will answer me."

So, with only a confidence that He could supply, "Okay, I'll ask Him, and I believe He will answer. It may not be the answer you want or understand, but He has the answer. Let's pray."

So, Crystal and I prayed with Bubby and asked God to give us the answer. We told her that the next time we visited we would tell her what God had said. We finished our time with our friend, gave hugs and kisses, and proceeded home for 40 minutes of mostly silent driving.

Crystal and I prayed again but didn't say much more that evening. I believed He was good, and that He would have an answer.

QUESTIONS
TO BE ANSWERED

The next morning, as I shaved, showered, and dressed, my mind was swirling with several things. First was Bubby's question. Second, "Is Sonny still alive?" Third, I needed to check on the custom fixture order.

Fortunately, I got up early and went down into my office to pray in my rocking chair. I longed to spend time in worship. As I sang a few melodies and thanked my Lord for His goodness, I felt God's presence in the room. I began to sing a song I learned in church over 35 years ago:

> *Majesty; worship His Majesty, unto Jesus be all glory, honor, and praise.*
>
> *Majesty, Kingdom authority, flows from His throne, unto His own, His Anthem raise.*
>
> *So, Exalt, lift up on high, the name of Jesus.*

Magnify, come glorify Christ Jesus the King.

*Majesty worship His Majesty, Jesus who died,
now glorified,*

KING of ALL KINGS

*Jesus who died, now glorified,
KING of ALL KINGS"*

(Capitol CMG Publishing, used by permission, used by permission)

God was with me, and I knew it. My Heavenly Father was embracing my words of praise. I could picture Jesus' sacrifice in my mind while feeling His compassion in my heart. The Holy Spirit was uplifting me with an enormous sense of His grace.

I asked the question, "Lord, what about Bubby's question?"

Though inaudible, I heard His reply: "Psalm 92." I turned to my Bible and started to read. Verses 1-4 acknowledged my plight as my Heavenly Father affirmed my thanksgiving and praise. Then came the answer; I knew as I began reading verses 5-7 that the answer was summarized in three concise statements:

*Oh Lord, how great are your works,
your thoughts are very deep.*

*A senseless man does not know,
nor does a fool understand this.*

*When the wicked spring up like grass,
and when all the workers of iniquity flourish,
it is that they may be destroyed forever.*

I knew this was God's answer for Bubby. In three verses, He established His sovereignty, rebuked Bubby's ignorance and lack of trust, and addressed the question: "If God is so good, then how could He let Hitler come into power so quickly and do all the evil he did, including the killing of so many Jews?"

God's answer: "When the wicked spring up like grass, and when all the workers of iniquity flourish, it is that they may be destroyed forever."

I received a swift and sensible answer that does not refute the facts. Yes, evil may flourish for a season, but God emphatically states His absolute and ultimate judgment of that evil.

God answered Bubby's question, and even though Bubby might argue, I knew there was no other response that was more complete. Not only was God talking to Bubby and answering her question, but He was also helping me grapple with the inevitable fate of Sonny. I was wrestling with what Sonny told me about his life purpose. I was logically thinking there could be another way, but God's ways are not our ways.

Now, I had to talk to Sonny. I went out my back door and started calling, first in a whisper, then in increasingly louder tones: "Son of Mantis, where are you? Sonny, are you here? Stop hiding from me," then in a demanding, frightened tone, "Sonny, where are you? Come out, please, please come out!"

Suddenly my eyes widened as something flew towards me. There was Sonny flying at me, landing on my shoulder. I was startled to say the least, "Sonny what are you trying to do, give me a heart attack?"

"No, just having some fun. I realized you hadn't seen me fly yet, so I thought I'd show off a bit."

He then flew off my shoulder to the rail of my deck, exclaiming in the process, "I love to fly. Usually I do it just to find my bride or when looking for a good meal, but I thought you would get a kick out of it. Sorry for the scare."

"It's okay. I'm a little jumpy lately. I'm really enjoying our conversations; I don't want them to end."

"Tom, that's the nicest thing a human has ever said to me."

"Really?"

"Absolutely. Of course, you're the only human I've ever talked with, so it's easy for you to win that prize. But now, tell me, why were you in such a huff? What's going on?"

"Last evening, we visited our friend, Bubby, and this 93-year-old Jewish woman asked a really hard question. She asked If God is so good, then how could He allow Hitler to come into power so quickly and do all the evil he did, including the killing of so many Jews?"

"And what did you say?"

"I said I'd ask God and get back to her."

"Tom, you're smarter than I thought. That's the best answer you could've given her. So, what did God say?"

"Are you sure He answered me?"

"When Jeremiah cried out to God with some tough questions, He said, 'Call to Me, and I will answer you, and show you great and mighty things, which you do not know.' God cares about you just as much as Jeremiah. So, what did He say?"

"He took me to Psalm 92:7 that says, "When the wicked spring up like grass, and when all the workers of iniquity flourish, it is that they may be destroyed forever."

"Boy, He gets right to the point, doesn't He?"

"And listen to the two preceding verses: 'Oh Lord, how great are your works, your thoughts are very deep. A senseless man does not know, nor does a fool understand this.' What do you think of that?"

"Nothing to argue about there. What do you think?"

"Well, I'm beginning to see that a lot of questions have answers we may not understand."

"You're a good student, Tom. Bubby's question isn't so different from the questions we all have. We all ask questions that we really don't need to be asking. God doesn't mind answering; however, He just may give us an answer that creates more questions. Now Tom, I've a question for you, one that may take some time and thought."

"Alright, Sonny, go for it."

"Are you ready — to die for your spouse?"

"Wait a second! Where did that come from? Is it because of your situation? You can't put me in your situation; I'm not a praying mantis. That's not fair."

"Yes, but you're a praying man. So, it is fair. Answer my question: Are you ready to die for your bride?'"

"Well of course, I love my wife. If placed in a dire circumstance, I would die for Crystal. Of course, I would do that for her."

"And your children, would you die for them?"

"Yes, I would die for them."

"But you're hoping that you'll never have to die for them, for your wife, for your children; am I right?"

"Yes, no one wants to die for someone else, or just die period, unless it's necessary, or God's timing. We all want to live as long as we can. God gave us life, and we should value it as precious."

"Absolutely, but sometimes that plan might be circumvented, especially if you're a praying mantis. He just wants us to trust Him."

"And you've helped me with that. You've been a great teacher."

"I'm glad you feel that way, so I have one more question: Tom, you say you're willing to die for your wife and your children. Now, are you willing to die for Him?"

"For Jesus?"

"Revelation 12:11 says, 'They overcame him [the devil] by the blood of the Lamb [Jesus] and by the word of their testimony, and they did not love their lives to the death.' There's evil in this world: Adam and Eve found that out. We're engaged in a battle. If He calls you to die a martyr's death, are you willing?"

"Boy, Sonny, this is serious stuff. I believe I am. I believe that I want God's will, not my own."

"And so do I, Tom. In the Garden, God gave the first couple everything they would ever need, but He also gave them a choice. They were deceived, just like Hitler or anyone that sells out to evil, but they had a choice. They could have gone back to the Father, their original source of life, questioning what the serpent said. God had the answers. The knowledge of good and evil doesn't replace trust and love. You are learning to rely on the only source of life that matters, and I'm proud of you."

"Thank you, Sonny. Now, let me ask you a question. How much longer will you be around? How much longer can I bounce this stuff off you?"

"Good question. I'm not sure. Autumn's finally here, and this is the time for the praying mantis to find a mate. I know my bride is close by, and we'll meet soon. Because of my willingness to be all God has designed for me, I believe you and I won't have much more time together. But may God's kingdom come, may God's will be done, right here in your backyard as it is in heaven!"

"Will we get a chance to say good-bye?"

"Not sure, I think we have a few weeks, so It's close, but not imminent. And speaking of time, did your custom fixture problem get taken care of?"

"Yes. I believe they are supposed to be shipped today. I'll go check on that. Thanks for reminding me."

Just then, I felt my phone buzzing in my pocket. I looked, and it was a hotel engineer who has been buying from me for close to 20 years. I took the call and talked to my friend Bill for several minutes. Fortunately, I had a pen and card in my pocket, so I wrote down some notes so I could research some needed product.

I turned around and Sonny was gone. I felt a little better knowing I would probably have a few weeks with him. Time is funny that way. We value it, yet we always want to get to the next moment. So off I went to work, taking one last look to see if I could say so long to Sonny, then headed to my van on the side of the house. I packed up the car with my briefcase and laptop, then backed out of the driveway.

Taking one last look at my gate as I backed out, there he was, on top of the fence, devouring a butterfly. Wow, another image I will never forget! Sonny has provided some unforgettable moments for me. When this is all said and done, I will be qualified to write a book, titled *The Balanced Diet of a Praying Mantis: Written by a Praying Man.*

14

"HI, NEIGHBOR!"

This day saw me resolve a lot of work situations. My custom fixtures were completed and shipped. The stores would all get what they needed before opening, so my customer was happy. My big parking garage fixture order was in the process of being shipped, and my friend Wesley would have his product at his buildings in time to supervise the work and get out of town for vacation. Wesley was happy.

Although my numbers were way down, I looked at my sales for the month and they were looking slightly better, so Crystal and I were encouraged. My day flew by, and before I knew it, the clock showed 5:45 p.m. Crystal was calling and telling me that dinner would be ready in 30 minutes, and I told her I would be arriving just in time. Then one last question from my bride: "Did you sell any light bulbs today?"

I just laughed and was on my way. Traffic was light

and I got home in 20 minutes. As I was pulling into the driveway, there he was. Sonny was on top of the fence as I got out of the car.

"Hi, neighbor!"

"Hi, Sonny, how was your day?"

"Two butterflies, a tree frog, three crickets, a fly, and a bee; It was an amazing day for hunting. I'm stuffed and ready to take a nap. How was your day?"

"Just as satisfying as yours. I got a lot of work done and saw some problems solved." Suddenly Sonny flew off. Crystal was coming out the side door and was surprised to see me.

"Tom, so you're home, I thought it was Faith out here. I was looking to take her car and go to the store, but since you're here, you can go for me."

"Honey, I just got out of the car, are you sure you can't go? I've had a long day, and . . ."

She just stared at me and I realized that nothing I could say would change her mind, "Okay, it would be my pleasure. What do you need?"

"That's better. I'm trying to finish dinner, but I realized I need some shredded cheese to put on top of my casserole, and it just wouldn't be the same without it, and we're out of coffee and milk. Can you remember shredded sharp cheddar cheese, milk, and coffee? Do you need me to write it down?"

"No, just text it while I get back in the car and go to the store."

She nodded, took out her phone and proceeded to text me the list. I started to back down the driveway when I looked over at my passenger seat. I was a little startled because there was Sonny smiling at me. He had flown in my open window unnoticed.

I shook my head and commented, "You know

you're getting into the habit of surprising me, but coming into the van? This is a first. Do you want to go shopping too? I thought you got enough groceries today?"

"Funny guy. No, I just thought this would give me some time with you when we wouldn't be interrupted. You got me thinking, Tom."

"I got *you* thinking?"

"Yes, I realize that I have a purpose whether I die for my spouse or not, even if I'm not consumed by her, my willingness and desire to serve her are enough."

"Really, so you won't have to die?"

"Well, I didn't say that, but what I am saying is that right now, I'm fulfilling God's purpose."

"How's that?"

"I'm obeying God. I'm loving Him and loving my neighbor as myself. According to Jesus, that's all God asks of us."

"Am I your neighbor?"

"Yes, you are, Tom. Do you remember Jesus' discourse about the Good Samaritan?"

"I think so. In one of the gospels, a man asked Jesus, 'Who is my neighbor', and Jesus told the parable of the Samaritan who helps the man who was beat up and robbed."

"Tom, Samaritans were enemies of the Jews. The injured man was presumably a Jew since he was from Jerusalem. So, a man's supposed enemy helped him when no one else would; even a priest and a Levite, two religious Jews passed by and avoided contact with the helpless victim."

"Okay, so our neighbor really could be anyone in need, anyone who God puts in our life, whether a friend or an enemy. Maybe even my customers?"

"Yes, even your customers. Whoever God has in

your life — your wife, your children, your grandchildren, Bubby, employers, fellow employees, your actual next-door neighbor, people you meet at church, or even at the grocery store picking up cheese for dinner. It could be anyone."

"I can't escape loving my neighbor, can I?"

"No, you can't. Do you remember a time when you were helped by someone you didn't know?

"Sure, lots of times, someone even helped me change a tire on the side of the road once, and you know, a few years later I was able to do the same for someone else."

"So, tell me, Tom. How were you able to love your neighbor as yourself? How could you think of some-one and care for them as much as you would care for yourself?"

"Hmmm, I guess my love for God helps me want to love others."

"As we learn to love God, spend time with Him, en-joy Him, worship Him with no religious strings attached, it becomes easier to love one another."

"So, it starts with God, and it ends with God; it's really not us, Sonny, it's Him."

"We may not admit it, but basically, we think life is all about us. That's why you really didn't want to go shop-ping now; you wanted Crystal to go, but you submitted to her request because it was easier to do that, rather than argue or debate. Am I right?"

"Sonny, I hate to admit it."

"Think about it; if we are most important, then no one else is important unless they can help us. We'll always think that we are right, we'll often take offense when there's a disagreement, and we'll never be satisfied."

I cringed. "That sounds very much like our world."

"Yes, however if we make everyone else more important than ourselves and treat them the way we would like to be treated, then we make a difference."

"Like Jesus."

"Jesus obeyed the Father and was the servant of all. He made everyone more important than Himself."

"Amazing." I made a right turn into the grocery store parking lot. "Thanks Sonny, I think you just made it a lot easier for me to be a good neighbor to my wife."

Sonny flew out the window, yelling, "See you at home."

I proceeded into the store, shaking my head over another conversation with an insect. Buying cheese, milk, and coffee never felt so good.

15

FORGET NOT ALL HIS BENEFITS

Crystal's casserole was amazing which made me quite happy I went to get that cheddar cheese. She made a quinoa dish that included ground turkey, veggies, and a breadcrumb topping topped off with a layer of cheddar cheese. It may not be something Sonny would enjoy, for it lacked tree frogs and insects, but it was a delight to Faith and me.

That evening, I decided to go out with my daughter and see what was going on in her life. Being that she was 23 going on 24, I figured that soon she would be out on her own, and after what she had gone through the previous year, I wanted to make sure we stayed close.

Last May 1, my daughter decided to go on an adventure to JeJu Island, South Korea. She had been a little antsy being at home when so many people her age had graduated from college and were starting careers.

Faith had been to college for two years, but realized it wasn't for her — at least for now. She had worked as a movie extra for nine months and then took a job as a nanny through an agency. She was ready for something different, so she applied to a non-profit organization to teach English to a little girl on JeJu Island for three months. She had been studying Korean for about a year, watching loads of Korean television, and was excited about living in another country, detached from Mom and Dad.

Crystal and I were apprehensive to see our little girl, although now a responsible adult, go so far away for so long. However, we prayed Psalm 91, a comforting prayer of protection over our daughter and asked God to send 27 angels to attend her. We came up with the number 27 because her birthday is October 27. With tears and laughter, we watched our baby board a plane destined for the other side of the globe.

After spending a week on the mainland in Seoul, she flew to her adventure on JeJu Island. Truth be told, this was just as much an adventure for me as it was for Faith. My little girl was 7,500 miles away and her days and mine were totally reversed. When she was waking up, I was going to sleep and vice versa. I never spent more time praying than while she was away, and I am so glad I did.

A week into her stay on JeJu, the real adventure began. I woke up early every morning, always anxious to turn on my phone to see a fun text, hear a voice mail, or see a video from South Korea. I always liked to wake up and touch base with Faith and pray with her before she went to sleep, and then I could go off to work, satisfied knowing that all was well.

I turned on my phone this day to receive a voicemail, however the words were very different, "Hey Mom and Dad, I'm alright, I guess I was hit by a car. I'm in the hospital. I'm pretty sure they won't have to amputate."

My heart sank, my stare became blank, and my insides screamed, "Amputate?"

What in the world? I immediately tried to call her back and was unable to get through. I prayed, "Dear Lord, be with my daughter. Protect and heal her. Take away all fear. Whatever's going on, please help her in any way she needs it."

Then I went into the bedroom to tell her mom. Crystal was soon awake, and I filled her in with the details. We were both reeling and needed to talk to our daughter and find out more.

After an hour, we were able to talk to Faith and get the lowdown. She was running across the street to catch a bus she was afraid she'd miss; the next thing she knew, she was laying on a grassy section near the street being attended to by emergency workers.

She had been hit by a car, and her left ankle had a compound fracture. Her bone was sticking out of her skin and she was awaiting surgery. She didn't remember the impact, although she apparently had been knocked out. She hit the ground so hard she was rendered unconscious until the ambulance and police showed up on the scene. She was very fortunate there was no concussion.

She had several doctors consulting before the surgery and that is where the "amputation" message came from. A young doctor felt it necessary to tell Faith that amputation was possible, but an older, wiser doctor shook his head and assured Faith that was unlikely.

From the time they heard of the accident, her host family had been working to arrange for a doctor they knew to perform the surgery. She had only been with them for one week, but they had no choice but to also join in on the adventure. I suppose God had an interesting plan for us all.

Faith's phone had run out of power and she did not have a charger with her, so I emailed her host family and asked them to notify us when the surgery was done and what the doctors related.

The host family consisted of a Mom (Minji), Dad (Sanghoon), and six-year-old girl (Sara). Education is very important in South Korea and they were depending on Faith to help Sara make some progress. Things were going well until today, but then time came to a halt.

Crystal and I prayed diligently and engaged our church and everyone we knew to pray for Faith. We weren't sure what was to be done or of the recovery time. We simply prayed for God's hand to direct all that took place. It was very difficult not being there: we didn't have the finances to fly to Korea on a moment's notice. As we prayed, we realized we could only wait.

The next day we got a short phone call and an email from Sanghoon assuring us of a successful surgery and explaining that soon Faith would have a charged phone and the ability to call us.

This was quite a test for Faith, who was in the hospital for close to six weeks. She ended up with a steel plate and eight screws in her left ankle and it took the entire time to grow the skin back enough to be discharged. What is most interesting is how God worked in Faith's body and in her spirit during this time.

At one point, they said they would need to see more progress with her healing, or they would still have to do a skin graft. Faith did not want to go through another surgery, so we prayed for supernatural skin growth.

Wouldn't you know it, from Friday to Monday we prayed fervently for quickened healing. When they looked at it on Monday, Faith said that the doctors' wide eyes told the whole story: "This is amazing how much the skin has grown in such a short time. You won't need a skin graft."

Everyone was encouraged, especially Faith. We had been praying Psalm 103 over Faith every day while in the hospital. This accident could have been so much worse, and Faith knew it. We were continually reminded of God's benefits. Towards the end of that Psalm, it says, "Bless the Lord, you His angels, who excel in strength, who do His word." We were confident that those 27 angels were watching over Faith as she healed in that hospital room, struggling with loneliness and pain.

At one point, she had a high fever, and they were concerned over the possibility of infection. I was never so proud of my daughter as I heard her digging into the book of Job and trying to understand how God is with you even when things get worse. She called me one evening when I was having dinner with a friend, and she prayed with us, explaining what she was learning. We all prayed together and within a few hours, her fever was gone.

We talked and prayed every day. My daughter and I grew closer; I hated that she was so far away, but I loved how we were interacting. Not all her time there was difficult; Faith made friends of the doctors and nurses and always had a story for us. A pipe in her hospital ward ceiling burst and she amused us with the activity that ensued as the "sky was falling." She somehow found ways to have fun racing down the hall in her wheelchair and standing out as the lone foreigner. White woman Faith stood out in this Korean Island hospital, and in many ways, she enjoyed the stay. However, when the time came for Faith to go back to her host family's home, she was ready.

The host family had a dog that Faith became great friends with, and Faith began to teach Sara the best that she could as she settled into life with a Korean family while still recovering. She was learning to get around on crutches and navigate life from a very different perspective. Her host family helped in every way they could, but Faith was a foreigner living amid expectations that were much harder to meet. And unfortunately, as Faith worked diligently to help Sara, she came to find that Sara did not want to learn. Faith was expected to do miracles in the midst of her own miracle rehabilitation, and the two did not mix very well.

As the days passed, unspoken issues began to mount, and Faith's visit became a roller coaster of good, bad, and ugly. Faith's American ways were misunderstood, and the whole subject of "manners" became very important. Sara became more and more difficult, and family issues that had nothing to do with Faith also began to arise. The adventure was ascending unto a mountain of frustration, and we were given many things to pray about.

After a few weeks back in their home, Faith was looking forward to going to church one Sunday morning. This was a Christian family, and we were happy that Faith would be able to attend church while in South Korea. In fact, during her hospital stay, she had gotten some encouraging visits from their pastor. So, after a couple weeks of recovery at home, Faith was finally able to navigate well enough to go with them, and she was looking forward to getting out.

As Faith was getting ready, she texted me with a disconcerting message. Sara was having a temper tantrum and was refusing to let Faith come with them. The family did not know what to do and it was apparent that Faith might not be able to go because of the bedlam that ensued.

Crystal and I were watching a movie in our family room (also known as my office) on a Saturday evening while Faith was preparing for church on Sunday morning. I was barely watching the screen since I was engaging Faith and praying via text as this battle continued. A Korean family and an American family were conducting spiritual warfare over a troubled little girl some 7,500 miles away.

There was a spiritual force trying to keep my daughter from going to church that morning, and it was not from God. A righteous anger rose up within me and I stood up from my rocking chair and exclaimed, "Tormenting spirit, leave that little girl in South Korea right now, in Jesus' name. You will *not* rule that family, you will *not* keep Faith from going to church. Be gone from them and do not return. Lord, cover that family with peace and have them go to church now knowing You love them. In the name and blood of Jesus Christ. Amen."

I just stood there frozen as I could sense in my mind's eye that God was at work. Within thirty seconds, I got a text from Faith. The little girl had stopped her tantrum and the household was peaceful. Faith was surprised at the sudden change of events, and they were on their way to church. This was not a coincidence, and my wife, daughter, and I understood a new dimension of faith that we had not experienced before. God has given the Christians authority, even over thousands of miles.

That turned out to be a great day for Faith, and Sara was at peace for several days, but by midweek Sara was back to being difficult while Faith and the family were frustrated. Over the next several weeks, more issues escalated, but things seemed to be working out until it was less than two weeks before my daughter's return to America. With an abrupt change of heart, Sara's Mom lost her temper and told Faith that she had to leave their home. Once again, it seemed like invisible spiritual forces were at work, and the next thing we knew, Faith was texting me from an Airbnb in the city, a few miles from the airport.

She still wasn't scheduled to leave for quite a while, and I was uneasy knowing that Faith was in a foreign country with no one to help her while she was in a hobbled state. Fortunately, Faith had just received an insurance settlement, so she had the resources to get a different flight. Unfortunately, it was impossible to find a flight on the same airlines any sooner and after much prayer and maneuvering, Faith booked a first-class flight that would reunite Crystal and I with our war-torn "baby girl."

A few days later, we were looking into the eyes of our youngest daughter and were never so happy to see her. She was gone for a little less than four months, but it might as well have been four years. As the United Airlines attendant wheel-chaired our daughter out through the airport construction tunnel into our arms, nothing could have been better.

So now, a little more than a year later, I was realizing that I needed to be proactive and spend time with my adult daughter. It is so easy to forget the importance of relationships and how God works in the midst of them. We had read and prayed over Psalm 103 so many times in the past year, remembering not to forget all God's benefits. As Faith and I ventured to find some ice cream and talk about everything or nothing, I was just enjoying being with her.

16

WHAT ARE
FRIENDS FOR?

I slept soundly that night and woke up at 5:30 a.m. As I measured the ground coffee with eyes at half mast, Crystal came downstairs and joined me to start the day. While the coffee was brewing, we prayed for our children and grandchildren, for people at church, for our neighborhood, and for each other. We opened the Bible and read about Jesus making a new friend: Zacchaeus, a tax collector, who He had called out of a tree. Jesus had just met Zacchaeus but had the nerve to tell Zacchaeus they were going to have dinner at his house that evening. Remarkably, it transformed the tax collector's life. After all, what are friends for?

The good ones change our lives in many ways. We studied the rest of the chapter as we sipped coffee. I fully awakened while Crystal made me three poached eggs, some toast, and half an avocado. The timing was perfect so I could leave for my appointments in an hour. I went upstairs and finished my routine.

As I got into my car, I kissed my bride of 37 years before backing out of the driveway and putting my windows up so I could turn on the AC. I was on my way to visit my customer, Sam, the maintenance supervisor at the Chateau Elan, about 75 minutes away. I was needed to identify some lighting fixtures that were not working and help him get the product replaced through a warranty. This property is amazing, consisting of a luxurious five-star hotel, spa, golf course, and vineyard.

As I was driving on Interstate 285 East, I realized that I needed to visit my friend Martin who was off the next exit and see if he needed any light bulbs before going on to Sam. As I pulled into a parking spot in front of Martin's building, I looked in the rear-view mirror and Sonny was staring at me. He had hitched a ride, and now we were both 20 miles from my house.

I wasn't startled like the day before, just curious. "What's going on, Sonny? Why didn't you tell me you were here? We've been driving for twenty minutes."

"I was wondering how long it would take you to notice."

"I didn't expect you. And I'm not sure I like the idea of you being so far away from my yard and your bride. What if you get lost?"

"You'll look after me."

"Of course, but I'm working and will be a bit distracted. You need to stay in the car."

"I can't do that Tom, not if you're going to put the windows up. Besides, I want to see you in action. Can I come with you?"

"Really Sonny? I guess, but how? You can't just sit on my shoulder and expect no one to see you?"

"Yes, I can, I'm the master of camouflage. I'll blend into your green shirt, and stay near your collar, near the lines. I'm stick-like, you know. Trust me, I blend in."

"Okay, I'm glad my first stop is with Martin. He's a good friend."

"This will be fun."

"I hope, but please, no matter what, don't talk to anyone."

"Don't worry, Tom. My mandible is sealed! Besides, you know I don't talk to anyone but you. You do know that, don't you?"

"I guess, but why's that?"

He didn't have time to answer for just then, Martin came around the corner, saw me in the car, and waved. Sonny hopped up on my left shoulder near the collar as I opened the door, picked up my briefcase, and greeted my friend.

"Martin, how are you? You hadn't ordered for a while so I just thought I'd stop by and see if I could help you."

"You must have been reading my mind. Come down to my shop and I'll show you a few things that we need, and then we can go to the room with the air handler. I need an occupancy sensor."

As I followed Martin, Sonny whispered in my ear, "I'm so excited, I've never been in a place like this. Tom, this is so much fun."

I just rolled my eyes as we went down a flight of steps, and soon we were in Martin's repair shop where he stored a supply of lighting and electrical items. I was very conscious of the Son of Mantis sitting on my shoulder, but he must have blended in because Martin was going about his business as usual.

I made a list of the things Martin needed and as I

finished, I looked in a small mirror that was in the shop at my shoulder. Sonny was not there. I kept looking in the mirror at different angles and twisted my head to see if I could see him, but then Martin looked at me funny. Martin was from Mexico and out of respect he called me Mr. Tom, "Mr. Tom, is there something wrong with your neck?"

"Sort of, I had a funny feeling, but uh, I'm okay. Let's go to the air handler." As we went out the door, I moved slowly and kept the door open a little longer than normal and then when I followed Martin to the next room, I did the same.

"What do you think, Mr. Tom? Is this room small enough to just have an inexpensive sensor to replace this wall switch?"

Just then I saw Sonny, in the corner of the room with a mouse between his jaws. I almost choked, and I put my briefcase down to hide Sonny and his recent meal. I took out my notebook, then I moved to a different part of the room so Martin would follow.

"Sure Martin, that would work just fine. Do you remember the sensors we put in the storage closets? This room's quite a bit bigger, but the same thing would work here. I'll get you one with the other products." I wrote that in my notebook, and silently prayed that Sonny had finished his snack.

"Okay, that's perfect Mr. Tom, and I also have a tenant that needs some lights. Come with me."

As I followed Martin, I first went to pick up my briefcase. I looked down and Sonny was still munching away. I looked at him wide-eyed and cleared my throat, motioning for Sonny to get back on my shoulder.

"Mr. Tom, are you sure you're okay? Do you need a bottle of water? Come to my office, I have a small refrigerator. I'll get you some water."

I followed Martin to the office as the door closed

behind me, and I did not see my insect friend on my shoulder yet. Martin handed me the water and I drank the whole bottle: I needed that. My mind raced, trying to figure out how to get Sonny back on my shoulder, "Martin, I need to go back to the air handler. I left my pen in there."

"I don't think so, Mr. Tom, it's in your pocket."

I looked down; it was in my pocket. "Yes, Martin, but my favorite pen, I must have left it in there, it isn't in my briefcase. My green pen, it's my favorite. Stay here, and I'll just look and see if it's there."

"Okay, but I'll follow you. We need to go to the tenant space."

As we walked to the air handler room, Martin opened the door with a key, and I rushed past him to the corner of the room seeing Sonny finishing the last morsel of mouse, I bent down and announced, "There you are, my favorite green pen."

Sonny hopped up onto my hand, and I opened my briefcase and slid my insect friend in as fast as I could. I shut it quickly. "Let's go, Martin, and see that tenant."

We went to the fifth floor and helped a radio station get some lights for track lighting in the hallways that highlighted the autographed album covers on the wall. I was anxious to finish and get back to my car. As Martin and I shook hands, I noticed a little blood on my right pinky, the same hand that Sonny was on.

Finally, I was back in the car. What was that blood? I was afraid to open the briefcase but knew that I had to. First, I wiped off the small remnant of blood with a paper towel and took a deep breath. I opened wide and looked down. I couldn't see anything, no Sonny, no anything.

As I looked through my briefcase which I opened and closed a dozen times every day, I was worried. I looked through one compartment, then another; I saw nothing. Then I heard, "Tom. Open up, it's hot in here!"

Coming from a spacious three-ring binder I had added yesterday came that familiar voice, "Neighbor, would you help me out here?"

"Sonny," as I opened it wide to see him in the middle of the three rings with pictures of lighting fixtures on either side, "You scared the daylights out of me. Are you okay? There was a drop of blood on my hand."

"I'm fine; my blood doesn't look like that. However, that was one of the tastiest field mice I've ever encountered. Thanks for taking me with you today. What's next?"

"First, let me use this hand sanitizer. I'm not happy to have mice guts on me."

Sonny chuckled, "I don't know why. I don't mind having mice guts inside me! Where to next?"

"The Chateau Elan, a first-class hotel on a very large property, including a golf course and vineyard."

"Sounds amazing, I'll bet that place has a lot of interesting delicacies!"

"Sonny, I didn't go to work today to introduce you to a new menu!"

Just then, I got a text from Sam, who had to cancel our appointment. I texted him back and said I would be back in the next couple days. "Sonny, we'll be going back home now; I don't need to see my customer at the Chateau. Sorry to disappoint you. Can you just behave yourself now and not give me so much concern?" As I looked to my right, there was Sonny eating a fly. I just shook my head.

Sonny smiled and said, "What? I didn't think you'd want to hear buzzing in the car all the way back home. I did you a favor. I mean, what are friends for?"

"Thanks Sonny, I can always count on you."

17

ESTABLISH THY THOUGHTS

Once I got home, the Son of Mantis returned to my backyard to munch on his normal array of creepy crawlies. I went into my ground floor office and glanced at a plaque that stood upright on my desk, "Commit thy works unto the Lord, and thy thoughts shall be established" (Proverbs 16:3).

I said a short prayer committing the rest of my day to Him and spent the remainder of it calling prospects off a list that my sales manager had given me. One of the other sales reps had recently retired and although his accounts were given to a new sales rep, many of the leads he was working on were given to me.

I was good at being persistent and not giving up on a lead until I got a response. Until I heard a definitive no, I kept calling on the prospect. Fortunately, more often than not, I would get an order and gain a friend. So, this day was full of phone calls, dozens of them. Out of all those calls, I got two appointments: One was close to my home in Acworth, at an assisted-living residence, and the other was a hotel near the Chateau Elan. I would be able to go visit the hotel when I had to go back and see Sam.

The assisted-living facility wanted to see me right away. In fact, it was part of a chain that had many facilities throughout Atlanta and was building more. I was hoping this would turn into something that would bring lots of business. I made a 10:00 a.m. appointment for the next morning.

I hadn't heard Crystal at all that day and was wondering if she had even thought of dinner. As I ascended my office steps up to the kitchen, I could smell something in the oven. My grumbling stomach was assuaged, but my curiosity was piqued. I reached to open the oven door, only to hear a rebuke from the other room, "Tom, get out of there. I'm roasting a chicken with potatoes, and we're having a salad. Could you go outside and get me some rosemary from our bush?"

If I didn't know better, I would think there were cameras everywhere. I replied with the utmost sincerity, "Yes, my precious bride. Is there anything else I can do for you?"

"No, the chicken has fifteen more minutes to cook, and I want to top it with some rosemary now to cook in some of that flavor. Thanks."

As I bent over the rosemary bush and plucked several sprigs, I jumped back as I almost grabbed something else. Amongst the rosemary bush was a small snake; something I had never seen before in our yard. I guess this was the year for critter surprises. As I pulled back, suddenly something else showed up. It was a praying mantis, and it wasn't Sonny. I had been spending so much time with him that I could tell the difference. The mantis grabbed the snake and began devouring its head. It looked up at me as if acknowledging my presence, then continued to eat.

I took a step back and stared at the mantis. Its abdomen was fuller, bigger. *This must be Sonny's bride*, I thought. Just then I heard my own bride, "Tom, where are you? How long does it take to get a handful of rosemary?"

I slowly backed off and tip-toed up the back-deck steps when I saw Sonny on the Impatiens staring down at his bride. He was totally enamored and didn't even acknowledge me. I couldn't stop so I went inside.

I took the rosemary to Crystal and she stripped the sprigs to sprinkle atop the chicken. She closed the oven door and handed me some napkins, "Set the table, my love. Dinner will be ready in fifteen minutes."

I proceeded to set the table and think about what I had just seen. Sonny was totally awestruck by his mate. He was on an emotional high, mesmerized by her beauty. I remembered what I thought of Crystal when we first met; I felt the same way. I remember what I thought of Faith when she was born, and held her for the first time. I remembered how I felt when I first came to know Jesus. I was in love and I had changed forever.

I was waiting for dinner, but my mind drifted back forty years. It was October 2nd, 1980. I had awakened from a twelve-hour surgery on my jaw and teeth. They had broken my jaw, cut out part of my bone and gum, removed both sets of teeth, and reset them, wiring it all together in a neat package.

I had been recovering from anesthesia for quite a while when I awoke suffocating. My mouth was wired shut and my sinuses were full of blood. My head looked like an overinflated basketball. I didn't know how to communicate with my mouth wired, so I pressed the button for my nurse and moaned as loud as I could. After several panicked buzzes and grunts, moans, and squeals, my nurse showed up, "What's your problem? Oh, don't you know what to do? Here, look at this machine. Stick this hose up your nose and it will suck out the fluids. Oh here, I'll show you."

At that, she stuck this long tube up my nose and turned the machine on, I saw blood and other liquids being sucked from my sinuses into this machine. She handed me the tube to do the other side. It was uncomfortable, and hard to maneuver. I was choking and draining myself with a machine that I had been introduced to two minutes ago. No one told me about this. It was awful.

As the morning progressed, things got worse. I was told after draining my sinus cavities that I was being discharged soon. I couldn't take the machine home, and the only help the nurse gave me was pain pills. When I told the doctor that I wasn't aware that this surgery was so intense, he said I would be okay, and my mouth would be unwired in three months. I couldn't picture being like this for three months. I was not in a good place. The next thing I knew my roommate, Kevin, was there to pick me up, complaining that he had to miss work to do this and was not happy that it took longer to sign me out than he expected.

Sitting in his car for the hour ride home from USC Medical Center to Lankershim Boulevard in North Hollywood, I wondered if I had made a mistake. I had just completed elective oral surgery on my jaw and teeth to correct an overbite so that my teeth and jaw would create the "Hollywood" image I was hoping for. I had braces on my teeth for the previous six years, but they had not done the job. I was pursuing an acting career in

Hollywood, and I was doing what I was told would correct my overbite, straighten my teeth, and give me an amazing profile.

I never thought of myself as vain, but since I had moved from Pennsylvania to pursue an acting career, I wanted to give myself the best shot. My original orthodontist back home was a great guy, but he gave me the impression that my braces were a two-year stint. Now six years later, I agreed to an experimental surgery, free of charge, arranged by my California orthodontist. He said it was the only way we could get the results I was looking for. With great enthusiasm, I agreed — until now. What did I get myself into?

That afternoon, I could not get comfortable, and Kevin, who had driven to California with me a year earlier with the same aspirations, was being a royal pain. I wanted my mother, but she was back in Baden, more than 2,500 miles away.

When evening came, my pain got worse. I tried some pain pills, to no avail. The pain was not letting up. I was having difficulty breathing, and I kept remembering the doctor saying, "Whatever you do, don't throw up. If you feel like you are going to throw up, here are some wire clippers. Unclip your jaw and then throw up. You don't want to drown in your vomit!" Nothing like that kind of encouragement.

Then Kevin started playing some hard acid rock. I didn't even remember him liking that kind of music, but for some reason he started playing music with a loud, screeching, pounding rhythm that had me hallucinating. I don't know if I ever felt worse in my life. It was probably earlier than 10:00 p.m., but I told Kevin I was going to bed where I shut the bedroom door to eliminate some of the noise.

I laid down and stared up at the ceiling. I had been in California for a year and had spent a lot of time praying. I grew up in a church environment that was traditional and religious, but I had strayed quite a distance since I was a child. This last year of isolation had me searching. I read a book by Charles Colson who was at the center of the Nixon administration Watergate fiasco. The title, *Born Again*, came straight out of John where Jesus told Nicodemus that "unless one is born again, he cannot see the kingdom of God."

I wasn't quite sure what all of that meant. I had read that book, and I was starting to read the Bible some, but I had so much going on, so much ambition, and so much confusion. And now, I was in so much pain, fear, and torment. Crying out to God, I began to sense the atmosphere changing, "God, I need Your help. I'm not just trying to make a deal, but if You take away this pain, I'll surrender to You. I give You everything about my life. Have Your way with me."

Like nothing I have ever felt before, a holy blanket descended upon me. That is the only way I can describe it. As I continued to pray and tell Him how sorry I was for my sin, I felt myself drifting off while the pain drifted also. I was in a different state of being than just minutes earlier. I began to sleep in heavenly peace.

When I awoke the next morning, it was a bright, sunny, Southern California day. I was feeling so good it was hard to understand. I didn't remember my prayer, at first. I just knew that I felt incredible, and that everything had changed. I got out of bed and went up to the mirror next to my dresser. I looked at myself, totally in awe. There was no swelling in my head. I could breathe freely; there was no pain at all. I went back to my bed looking for drained blood and fluids. It was dry with no sign of any of that. I was amazed. Then I went back to the mirror and looked at myself more intently than ever before. *This must be what they mean about being born again.*

I felt alive spiritually, and God had healed me physically. It was a miracle. I was totally in love with God, and I had so much hope. I began to read my Bible and tell others about Jesus. From that time on, my way of thinking changed drastically. I have never been the same since.

"Tom, go wash your hands before dinner. Faith just got home from work. Let's eat." Crystal's voice startled me from my daydream, and I went downstairs to wash.

I sniffed my rosemary drenched hands before washing. I loved the smell of rosemary; it is my favorite herb. It reminded me of my insect friend outside staring at his bride. Then with clean hands, I ascended to dinner to join my daughter and my bride for some rosemary chicken.

18

"LOOK UP"

I went to the assisted-living appointment the next day and got a good first-time order. The maintenance man liked me, and I got a promise from him to help me get into the corporate office if he was happy with our service. I felt like I was on a roll, so I decided to go see several of my nearby existing customers. I worked my way through one town to the next, picking up several orders. I did the same over the next few days, exhausting my local business opportunities.

Before visiting Sam at the Chateau Elan, I went across the street to the Baymont Inn. This was my other phone appointment. I was able to help with some security lighting on the perimeter of the building, so I got another new account.

I was having fun. The sales profession can be a lot of fun when you are making sales. However, when you are not, it's quite the opposite. To tell the truth, I never really wanted to have a sales career, but God had a different plan for me.

I had worked at a dozen different jobs over a few years, and was struggling as a young actor in Hollywood. I had already surrendered my life to Him and began to realize He wanted me to lay the acting aside and seek His future for me. I was having a lonely day, so I started to worship and pray. I began to cry out, "God, I'm lonely, I'm ready for a lifetime mate. I'm ready for a career. I'm ready for whatever You want for me — whatever wife, whatever job."

I guess that is how you get your prayers answered: letting Him choose. In less than two weeks, I met Crystal and the founders of the company I still work for now. I prayed allowing God to choose and poof — here I am 38 years later, married to the same woman and in the same job. And they have both been good to me; not always easy, but just like God, always good.

So, as I left the Baymont Inn and ventured across the street to help Sam, I looked over Sam's vast property: The Chateau Elan is a world of its own. The five-star hotel was just remodeled, and if I knew what the Taj Mahal looked like; I'd say it looked like the Taj Mahal. There was a day when I could afford to stay in a hotel like this, but not lately.

I found Sam, and we went to the golf course and into the retail area where they sold expensive golf shirts. Over one of the racks were several down light cans that were not emitting light. Unfortunately, this was a remodeled area, and they could not find the plans, so I had to get on a ladder and take the fixture apart to find out the model numbers.

It took a bit of maneuvering, a flashlight, and my amazing phone camera to determine the part numbers.

I got what I needed and emailed the information to the correct manufacturer to get price and availability and warranty information. When I began my career, it would have taken a few hours to find the information and do an inquiry like this, but now within minutes I could finish my work.

As I walked out of the golf shop and returned to my car, I looked across the vast property that stretched out for quite a distance and included a vineyard. I was glad I had not taken Sonny there. The property was huge, and if he had gotten lost, especially in the vineyard, I would never have found him. There are probably enough creepy crawlies and critters to keep Sonny and his bride munching for weeks until it was time for the inevitable.

When I got home that evening, I set my heart on going outside after dinner to look for Sonny. It had been more than a week since I had seen him. As my wife did the dishes and Faith went out to visit friends, I slipped out to the back deck. I explored the back yard and returned to the deck concerned that I may have seen the last of the Son of Mantis. I sat on the deck staring at my favorite New Guinea Impatiens when from behind a leaf, there popped Sonny's head, "Hi Neighbor, long time no see! What've you been up to?"

"Sonny!" I rejoiced, "I've missed you."

"And I've missed you, Tom. Did I see you out here last week when my bride caught that snake? Wasn't that beautiful?"

"Yes, Son of Mantis, that was beautiful. You were mesmerized. I couldn't wait for you to come out of your trance. I was helping Crystal."

"Sure, your bride is important too; I'm so glad you aren't neglecting her."

"Thanks for your assistance, Sonny. Watching you

has helped me become much more aware of how special she is. She's uniquely perfect as my bride."

"Touché' Tom, you're being shaped into His image. So, where have you been? How's your business? How'd your big fixture order and custom fixture project turn out?"

"Really well; both are finished. Wesley's fixtures were installed on time and everything on the custom fixture project is done, shipped, and installed. You really helped me with the right mindset."

"No problem, Tom. What are friends for?"

"You said that to me before. We really are friends, aren't we?"

"Absolutely, you're the only human I've ever spoken with. I've enjoyed it immensely."

"That reminds me. I was asking you about that last week. Sonny. Why me? Why did you decide to talk with me?"

"You're a God seeker, and I recognized you needed a little direction. Otherwise, I have nothing to say to humans. Besides, Jesus said it all in the gospels, showing us the will of His Father. God gave us His Son, and He invites us all to the wedding."

I thought out loud, "Yes, the wedding." Then looking intently at Sonny, "Speaking of weddings, what about yours? Where's your bride? How soon's the big date?"

"I'm not exactly sure, no mantis knows the day or hour, but I can discern the time. It's near."

"Sonny, how do you do that? I had a long drive home from the Chateau Elan, and I was thinking of the book of Revelation and the end times. Whenever I'm thinking of something biblical, you start speaking in a way to advance the conversation."

"Wait a second, Tom, you went to the Chateau Elan, and you didn't take me?"

"Yes, sorry Sonny, but don't change the subject. Apart from your appointment with your bride, do you think Jesus is coming back soon for His bride?"

"Good question, Tom. Every generation since Jesus' Ascension has been asking that. What do you think?"

"Well, there's a lot described in the Bible that looks like current events: the confusion and unrest in the world, plagues, wars. Things aren't getting better, are they, Sonny?"

"Doesn't seem like it."

"If you're interested in astronomy, you would notice some unusual heavenly signs, not to mention there have been global economic issues; it seems like everything's coming to a head."

"Then look up. Jesus very clearly talks of these things in Luke's Gospel. 'Your redemption draws near. You can discern the season. Look up — every day, every hour, every minute.'"

"But Sonny, it's so hard to keep focused on Him. There's so much pulling us away."

"Tom, when Jesus came, He said the same thing as John the Baptist. 'Repent for the Kingdom of God is at hand.' Nothing's changed. Jesus is the same, yesterday, today, and forever. The Kingdom of God is at hand, right now. There are two kingdoms operating in this world. We need to make a choice; salvation isn't about just going to heaven someday. It's about choosing the right Kingdom, His Kingdom, now."

"Thanks, Sonny, I'm realizing that more every day."

"Tom, everything around you shines forth the glory of God. You just need to open your eyes and look up, and it's our job to help others do the same."

My cell phone, sitting on the deck table, vibrated

with a text. I looked down to read the text, "Come out to the front porch, Tom. You should see the sunset; the sky is gorgeous."

"Sonny, you won't believe what Crystal just texted me."

"Tom, you keep forgetting about my eyesight. Go to Crystal. Run, go out front with your bride and together, look up!"

19

THE KING OF GLORY

The next day was Saturday and it was glorious. Light was streaming through the window as I awakened around 8:00 a.m. Keeping a sales schedule for many years and rising early every day helped me appreciate weekends. I went downstairs, drank two glasses of water, which is my daily habit, and got a cup of coffee that my bride had already prepared. I ventured to the back of my house to pray and read my Bible.

We have a patio area outside my office door with some cushioned lawn chairs that I love to sit in while reading and praying. From that vantage point, I can watch my wife's bird feeders being swarmed by a variety of finches, cardinals, thrashers, and catbirds. The area is still cool and shady, and the atmosphere is perfect for study.

But this day, I was distracted. I looked out across my backyard and saw my wooden fence tilted forward. I had viewed this problem previously, but it seemed to be exacerbated. Then I looked to my right and saw part of the fence caving in. I got up and examined the entire perimeter of the yard to find several other areas with issues, including the gates on each side.

Something had to be done, but what? I knew I couldn't afford a new fence, but I had to consider it, so I called my friend, Bobby, from church. He has experience with every type of house situation, both inside and out. I thought he might have some answers, so I made an appointment for him to come by the following week.

I felt good about taking this action, so I was no longer distracted. It was time for God and me. I began worshiping with a song I learned many years ago based on Psalm 42: "As the deer pants for the water, so my soul longeth after thee, You alone are my heart's desire, and I long to worship thee."

Those words are precious to me; I learned them when I first came to know Jesus and my desire for intimacy with Him was fresh. Now 40 years later, I was experiencing a renewal that made me feel the same.

After prayer and reading the Bible, I felt God was showing me what to do with the fence and that was wanting to take that fence down. The more I thought about it, the more I was convinced. So, I told Crystal what I was thinking.

I didn't expect her reaction, but she was vehemently opposed to the idea. Her flower beds looked great against the fence. The yard had been enclosed since Faith was a little girl, and Crystal had adapted all her gardening within the confines of a fenced-in yard. I tried to explain that I felt like this was just not my idea, but that God was instigating this, with little effect. In fact, at one point in our discussion, things got a little heated.

So, what do you do when your wife feels strongly

about a subject, and you feel the opposite? Do you insist on your way? Do you play the "submit to your husband in all things" card, which never works, or cave in to her will? What to do? I told her I would think about what she was saying and then walked to another room. I prayed that God would reveal clearly what He wanted for both of us.

I forgot about the dispute as the next week commenced, bringing on the usual business. Before we knew it, I was home Thursday morning, awaiting Bobby and his evaluation of our fence. He explained that because of the deep roots of all the neighboring trees affecting the alignment, it would be expensive to rebuild.

Then I told Bobby what I was feeling about bringing the fence down. He agreed and then prayed with me. I had him explain the situation to Crystal so she could see the practical reasoning for removing the fence. She listened to what Bobby had to say, and I figured that would solve the argument. I asked Bobby how much it would cost to take the fence down, and he said he'd get back to me. As Bobby said goodbye, I was satisfied.

I smiled and looked at my wife who wasn't smiling. She was more adamant than ever: that fence was not coming down! It was too important for the landscaping; she couldn't picture our yard without it. We bantered back and forth for several days, and we prayed. When Bobby got back to me with the cost to take down the fence, money I didn't have, we concluded that we would leave it up for this season and take it down at a future time. I guess I heard wrong concerning the fence coming down.

However, a few days later, Crystal got up to find that the main gate of the fence, on the right side of the house had fallen. This was the same gate where I first talked with Sonny. Like a drawbridge, that gate fell forward, disconnected from the rest of the fence. God was showing us what to do. As we discussed it, Crystal and I realized that the fence was supposed to come down, but only in the areas where it was falling. We felt we were to remove the gates and the fence in every troubled area but keep the corners of the fence so Crystal's landscaping would still work. It was the perfect compromise, and the Lord orchestrated it.

As we thought more about the solution, we realized it was perfect, except for one thing. Money was tight, and we didn't have the $500 needed to take the fence down. So, we prayed and set a date for Bobby to show up. I knew this needed to be done, so we figured we would delay or shuffle a few bills to make it work. A few days beforehand, while opening the mail, there was an envelope from a friend out in California. In the envelope was a check for $500. I guess God wanted that fence down as much as I did.

That evening before retiring, I opened the Bible to Psalm 24. That psalm is about how God shows up for those that seek His face. Verse seven says, "Lift up your heads, O you gates! And be lifted up you everlasting doors! And the King of glory shall come in."

Weeks later, when the fence was down, we took the gate that fell forward and painted that verse on it. We placed it strategically in our backyard so we would never forget. My bride and I are learning together, even after 37 years of marriage, that every issue, small or large, is an opportunity for "The King of Glory" to come in.

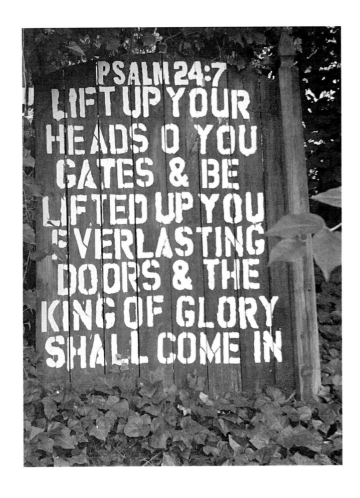

MY HERO

When the fence came down, both Crystal and I were pleasantly surprised. It opened our yard and made it look twice as big while creating some contrast where we kept the fence. We could see our neighbors' yards, creating relationship opportunities for the first time in 18 years. I met my neighbors to the back and left of us. Perhaps we should have done this long ago.

The next weekend, when I was enjoying my fence-less yard, a thought came to me. I hadn't seen Sonny or his bride in more than a week. Did the fence removal drive him away? Was the fence keeping him in?

That's absurd, I thought, *Sonny can fly. He could have flown away any time.* But then, I realized that he was there because he followed his bride. There was such an abundance of insects and critters because of Crystal's vegetation, which is why his bride chose our yard. But now she could venture out to other yards that may have a new variety of creepy crawlies. In fact, I read that the female mantis can't fly as well or at all like the male, but now she was free to roam with the fence down.

I didn't want to be selfish, but I began to pray, "God, I would really like to see Sonny and his bride again. I know the fence coming down was your idea, but I also miss Sonny."

I sat down in the back, finding my favorite cushioned lawn chair, but this time I sat facing the house instead of the back. I was next to the grill, so I was hidden from the birds, as they came swooping past me. I would often watch them going to the feeder or the bird bath to the right just below the back deck.

I was watching a nuthatch getting a mealworm from one of our feeders when I saw another nuthatch fly to the ledge of the feeder. The first one tilted down and fed the other. I had often seen the cardinals feeding each other and sometimes feeding one of the juveniles, but this was the first time to see the same with a nuthatch.

Crystal had taught me a little about our flying friends, and we have a book about Georgia birds that I occasionally looked at. I really enjoyed the birds. Just then, I saw another animal that didn't notice me sitting behind the grill. A cat was sneaking in toward the feeders; I suppose he was after a bird.

But then I saw her; Sonny's bride was in the monkey grass below the feeders. She was feasting on a grasshopper. I froze, not sure what to do. The cat was sneaking in on something. Was it a bird, or Sonny's bride? The cat was slow, but methodical, preparing to pounce.

Suddenly, he pounced and was headed right toward Sonny's bride. From out of nowhere, Sonny flew onto the scene and attached himself to the cat's ear. Those prickly claws of Sonny's dug in, and Sonny took a bite: The cat screeched with an unearthly sound and did a front flip, batting at Sonny the whole time. His bride sprang up onto a plant on the side of our deck to a safe place. All the birds flew away, and Sonny was wrestling with the cat.

The feline batted Sonny off, and as he was tumbling, the cat poised, ready to devour my good friend. That's when I intervened. As I got up from the lawn chair, I caught Mr. Meow's attention. He scampered out through the hole in the back that recently supported a fence. Sonny looked shaken as I approached. "Sonny, are you okay?"

"Now I am. I could see that cat's tonsils. Thank you."

"You know, Sonny, that was pretty brave of you. I saw you save your bride. That feline was two feet from her. And you know she's right above us looking down here. Have you two met yet?"

"No, Tom, it isn't appropriate. I've only watched her from a distance. We aren't supposed to meet until the appointed time."

"Well, she's looking at you now. See the planter on the side of the deck. You enabled her to escape there. Maybe we should meet her." Before Sonny could convince me otherwise, I stood up and looked at her eye to eye. Sonny just stared up from the ground.

"Hello, Miss Mantis, I'm Tom. I know you've seen me before, but we've not been formally introduced. Your friend down there who saved your life talks to me. Can you talk to people also?"

She cocked her head, much like Sonny did the first time we met, but this time, I didn't turn away. I stood there looking at her, waiting. She cocked her head the other way and then walked to the edge of the planter toward me as though she was about to speak. Then she leaped downward and landed on the head of the St. Francis of Assisi statue right next to where Sonny was perched. She made a short skip down to where Sonny stood. She came up to him face to face, and I braced. Was this the end? Was she about to devour him? I knew I couldn't interfere; this was between two of the same species. I just stood there watching.

Miss Mantis methodically walked around Sonny in a circle and then came back to him head-to-head. She touched her head to his and then bounded off toward the island of bushes in the back of my yard. Sonny looked up at me and exclaimed, "Wow, isn't she wonderful? Did you see that?"

"What, did I see what? She ran off, that's what I saw."

"No, she was thanking me. She acknowledged me, and you."

"Really? Is that what she did?"

"Tom, you shouldn't have approached her like that. It wasn't your place."

"I'm sorry. I guess I've gotten a bit too familiar with you. I assumed she would be grateful that you saved her and then that I saved you. I figured she'd talk just like you."

"It isn't time yet for her and me, and apparently she isn't interested in beginning a friendship with a human being. She has no reason to converse with you. I would have been surprised if she did."

"I get it Sonny, but now where did she go? Have you two left my yard since the fence came down?"

"Yes, we have, but we haven't found any yard as abundant in nourishment as your yard. We'll stay here; we have your yard mapped out pretty well. We know exactly where to hang out for what type of snack. You've supplied us with a veritable smorgasbord. I'm staying close to my bride for the time is near. If you see me doing my fancy Son-of-Mantis dance for her, you'll know that it's time for us to make disciples."

"Make disciples? That's a funny way to put it."

"Yes, that's what I call it: reproducing those like myself. It will be time for us to produce a bunch of little mantises, and it could be hundreds."

"That's wild. If humans had hundreds at a time, the world population would grow way too fast. And of course, think about all those diapers!"

"Funny guy. We must produce hundreds or at least dozens for our species to survive. They get eaten by other insects, frogs, birds, and each other. They disappear quickly, so the quantity is important. So, it was very important that you took that fence down. It creates an avenue of escape for the offspring."

Just then, my backyard neighbor, Myles, who didn't know I existed two weeks ago came walking through his yard to mine. He waved and called out, "Tom, I was wondering if you could come over and give me a hand. I found a small couch for my family room at the consignment store, and I need some help to bring it in."

"Of course, I'd love to help, I'll be over in a second. I need to change my shoes."

Sonny disappeared, and I proceeded into the house and quickly changed my sandals into tennis shoes. As I told Crystal where I was going, I added, "I'm going to ask Myles and his wife to come to our Bible study this week. I think they might be interested. It's time we purposely try to make more disciples." I laughed to myself, *If she had only heard my conversation with Sonny.* "And Crystal, even if they can't come this week, let's invite them to dinner soon."

"Perfect, my precious husband. Did you know you're my hero?"

"Really? Where did that come from?"

"Tom, you've always been my hero. I love how you reach out to others; you know how to be a friend. From the day I met you, you've been my best friend. Your love and friendship have rescued me in many ways."

I took Crystal by the hand and gave her a kiss. "I'll do my fancy dance later."

Looking at me sideways, Crystal smirked, "What does that mean?"

"Gotta help Myles. See you in a whiles!" Then I pranced out the back door through my fenceless backyard to lift a couch and perhaps help make a disciple.

21

"GO INTO ALL THE WORLD"

My discussion with Sonny and my statements to Crystal about making disciples had me thinking, especially about all my children and grandchildren. Jesus' words to "go therefore and make disciples" was one of His last statements while on earth. At one time, I thought there were two kinds of Jesus followers—disciples and then just every-day Christians. As I started studying Jesus' words, "Repent for the Kingdom of God is at hand" and His constant reference to that Kingdom, I had the revelation that I must surrender to the King if I am to be part of His Kingdom. I had to allow myself to be discipled out of this world's kingdom into His.

The first disciples left their nets and families to follow the King and become "fishers of men." I must do the same. I mean, for Heaven's sake, an insect went out of his way to help disciple me, the least I could do was reach those closest to me.

We all need someone to help us understand who God is. Jesus would never have left the realm of heaven unless that was true. I love being a father, realizing that a big part of that is introducing my children to our heavenly Father. Three of my four children were adopted, but they do not have to feel like orphans. They can feel the security of God's care no matter where life leads them.

When Amber and Alicia, my twins, first came to live with us, they had just turned eight years old. As I transported them from their last moments of foster care to our permanent home, Alicia blurted out, "Hey Tom, I've got a good idea. How about if we call Crystal 'Mom' and you, 'Dad'? What do you think?"

Everyone needs to and wants to belong to a family. Everyone needs a father they can trust. The deepest desire of my heart is to see my children and grandchildren know they can trust God. I worked hard to make that happen as they grew up, but I came to realize that I wasn't always purposeful, and sometimes I was religious and heavy handed. Also, I expected the Sunday School teachers and the Christian schools to fill in the gaps. I was very involved with church and Christian ministries, but I wished I had spent a little more time praying for them and asking God what to do next.

Since my girls began having children, I've realized that although I don't have quite as much time with them, God has given me special moments with this next generation that they will always remember. So, when I get the chance, I do my best to show them God's love. You don't always know what that means until the opportunity arises.

A few years back, my oldest granddaughter,

Marina, who now lives in Tennessee, lived in Pittsburgh, but she would go to Tennessee to be with her Dad in the summer. Since we lived only a few hours south of her Dad, we got the opportunity to have her for a couple of days. This particular year, as we traveled back to our house, I sensed that Marina was troubled.

Marina and I were at the kitchen table talking about life in general, and I decided I would cheer her up and have a little fun. Because the squirrels in our yard were quite prodigious and a nuisance in many ways, I would throw golf balls at them to shoo them away. I went to my back deck and reached in the bag with the golf balls, and yelled out, "Marina, watch this."

She looked out the window and watched as I tossed a Titleist in a nice high arc toward my target. In the year that I had been doing this, I had never hit a squirrel. But with Marina watching, wouldn't you know it. I hit one right in the skull! That squirrel did a flip and landed on his back with his feet in the air. I killed it. I couldn't believe my eyes.

I ran into the house and saw a terrified and confused Marina staring at me. "You killed that poor innocent squirrel, Pop Pop. I can't believe you did that!"

I was flushed and stunned, "Marina, I'm so sorry, I was just trying to show you how I shoo them away, but that's the first time I ever hit one. I'm so sorry you had to see that. Come with me, let's go down there and see if he can be helped."

I took my teenage granddaughter by the hand and we proceeded to the scene of the crime. As we came closer, we could see that he was not moving. I felt terrible. Then I remembered a story I heard many years back about the actor/singer Pat Boone praying for one of his children's pet mice. So, I took Marina by the hand

and smiled, "Marina, the Bible says in Matthew 18:19 that if two agree on earth concerning anything that the Father in heaven would do it. Marina take my hand, and let's agree. *Lord, I'm so sorry for bringing down our little friend here, forgive me and please have mercy on us. Lord, we agree according to this scripture that You will revive this squirrel and heal him, in Jesus' name.*

If I hadn't seen it, I wouldn't have believed it. One of that squirrel's little back legs started twitching, then the other. I said, "Let's keep praying. Lord, we agree in Jesus' name that You will raise up this squirrel. Lord, heal him!"

His front legs twitched and, in a minute or so he went from his back to his feet. I encouraged Marina to pray now, "Go ahead, Marina, you pray."

From that 16-year-old mouth came a prayer of faith, and I saw the restoration continue, "I agree with Pop Pop, God, help this squirrel keep moving. Be healed squirrel, in Jesus' name!"

He slowly moved more and more until finally, as Marina prayed behind him, the squirrel went running up a tree and it was obvious that heaven had invaded earth.

Marina and I laughed and went into the house, and it opened up a conversation that eventually led us to go downstairs to my office and have a good time praying and dealing with some very important issues. God used the prayers for the squirrel to lead to many more. At any given moment, God opens a door that otherwise may be locked. Discipleship doesn't need to be a classroom subject or a purposeful Bible study. The best opportunities to disciple are real-life scenarios that just happen.

During the past year, I prayed that somehow we would get a chance to visit all ten grandchildren, and wouldn't you know it, from Florida to North Carolina to

Tennessee to California, we saw all ten and shared some beautiful moments. That may not be as dramatic as a squirrel resurrection, but precious just the same.

Now, the next day my 15-year-old grandson, Conner, came to spend some time with me. Normally, Conner lives in Florida with his mom, but currently he was visiting his dad in Georgia. I cherish every moment with him since it is usually just once or twice a year.

This evening, Conner was bent on shooting my pellet rifle at a can hanging from a tree in the backyard. We have done that many times when Conner visits, but I never had insect friends living in my backyard before. I wanted to make sure they were out of harm's way; a stray pellet would not be healthy for Sonny or his bride.

I perused the area thoroughly before mounting the can. I was pretty sure that Sonny and his bride were not close by so we proceeded to shoot the tin out of that can, literally; I took two shots, then Conner until there was very little left. As Conner was shooting the last bit of metal from that can, I looked to the left and saw Sonny laying back on a Hosta leaf watching the demonstration. He looked over at me and winked his approval. Then he grabbed a cricket that just happened to be too slow for the show, and the Son of Mantis snacked while we shot.

Conner got some cans of sparkling water and placed them down at the base of our big bird bath. We shook them up and then shot them to see if they would explode. They didn't explode but Conner had a great idea. He has slow motion on his new cell phone, and we recorded him shooting the carbonated water can in slow motion as it rolled down the hill into the other. Action film makers had nothing on us that evening. We were making a memory, just enjoying the time together. That's part of discipling, too.

Sonny sat back and enjoyed Conner and I as we shot and laughed and bantered about nothing until the fireflies showed up. It was a little late in the year for fireflies, so I was a bit surprised to see them, as was Conner, but he chased a few and caught them in his hand.

"Look, Pop Pop, it's lighting in my hand."

"You know when I was a kid, we called them lightning bugs."

Just then Sonny couldn't help himself; right in front of us, he leaped and caught a firefly and landed on the little table next to where we were sitting. As Sonny devoured, the insect stayed lit and it glowed in his mouth as Sonny munched. Conner and I were stunned and watched intently. I was worried about what he would do. But with a burst of laughter, Conner blurted out, "How cool is that! A praying mantis eating a lightning bug! Awesome!"

We watched until Sonny was done, and then Sonny flew off to find some more. Sonny gave us a memory to talk about for a lifetime. Whether he knew it or not, Sonny set up some good discipleship moments for the future.

22

I BELIEVE IN MIRACLES

Conner slept over that night, but I had to take him back to his father's the next morning. I prayed for him as he left my van, we hugged, and he was off. I drove to one of my customers, a private Christian school, that had just bought a large order from me a few months ago to retrofit much of their lighting. William, the director of maintenance, and I had forged a friendship, and we prayed for one another. There is nothing better in my world than being able to sell lots of light bulbs, talk about Jesus, and top it off with prayer.

We had a great visit, went to lunch, and I introduced some new UV lighting to clean their air handling units and disinfect the air. He had to return some extra product he couldn't use, so I drove to my local warehouse to drop it off and make sure a credit was issued for the return.

It was the end of my month and my numbers were not anywhere near my goals, so handing in a return was a little disheartening. I took care of business and got back in my car to go home mid-afternoon. I planned to sit down at my desk at home, make a few phone calls, and send out some quotes.

As I was driving home, I got a call from a contractor trying to get me to lower my pricing on a project I had quoted yesterday. When I asked him a few questions, I discovered that he had given out my prices to another vendor and the vendor went much lower. Now the contractor was seeing if I could even go lower than that. It seemed as if the other vendor was offering an inferior product, so we discussed that.

He asked me to send a new quote taking part of the product off the order, and he said he would order part from me and some from the other vendor. I called my project manager and explained what he needed to do for the re-quote. When I was just about to turn up my driveway, I heard a ding on my phone and knew that my project manager had sent the quote. As I turned off the engine, I looked at the phone and saw it was done.

I got my computer out of the car and set up my office. I got a bottle of water and sat at my desk. As soon as I opened my computer and started to look at another quote I was working on, I saw a new email. It was the contractor. He said that he was canceling the order all together and they decided to go with the other vendor.

I was so upset I could have spit. I had been working on this quote with my project manager all week and we had put a lot of time into it. I was not going to let this go without a fight. I stood up and paced as I called the contractor. I opened the door going to my outside patio and sat down on the cushioned chair, and waited several rings before he picked up, "Hey, Andrew, this is Tom Borga, I just got your email, and I was surprised. I thought the other vendor was quoting an inferior product; that's how they got lower. Have you decided to go with that?"

"Sorry Tom, they assured me it was the same thing, and the owner saw the difference in price and ordered from the other vendor. I'm sorry, but it was the owner's decision. Maybe I can order from you the next time. Let's talk in the future." Click. That was the end of the conversation.

How could I lose that order? My month was almost over, and my sales were way down. I was depressed. I sat on my patio chair looking out into space. I took a deep breath and sighed.

Sonny popped out of the flowerpot on the table beside me, "What's your problem, Mr. Gloomy. If I didn't know better, I'd think you lost your best friend."

"You're my best friend, and yes, I think I'm about to lose you, but that's not what's bothering me most right now. I'm having a bad month, and this is turning into a trend. I'm not sure what to do Sonny. I like where I work. Sales can be stressful, but I've been with the same company for 38 years. I don't have the money to retire, and I know I can still be productive. What if they ask me to retire; force me out to pasture? What will I do?"

"Tom, you're not just another man struggling with a work situation, you're a praying man. I may be a praying mantis, but you're even more amazing: You're a praying man. What should you do?"

"Pray and expect a miracle? That's what I need right now, a miracle."

"Well, you believe in miracles, so what's your problem? You've experienced miracles. You've come to know that, with God, all things are possible."

I was feeling slightly encouraged. "Sonny, I know, all that's true, but . . ."

"But what? This is the perfect set up for a miracle. I'm a miracle, Tom. Our interactions are part of a miracle. In the Bible, when the donkey talked to Balaam, do you think that was a normal interaction between man and animal? That was a miracle. God gave that donkey discernment and a voice for a purpose. It's the same with me right now. Our time together is a miracle. Don't start doubting now!"

"Wow, you're right."

"And Tom, the bigger miracle is man. Man was made in the image of God, not the image of a donkey or a praying mantis. God made the animal kingdom and everything that creeps on the earth for mankind, to serve God's purpose for man."

"So, what are you saying, Sonny? What are you thinking?"

"Mankind may have lost God's image with Adam's sin, but now with Jesus' life in you, it's regained! God's creativity is within you. If you must leave your company, or if God has something different for you after this long, fruitful career, what would you like to do?"

"A lot of things, I guess."

"Tom, let me help you. Look at your life. You prayed for a wife and a career and within weeks He gave you both. Do you know what a miracle it is that you're with the same company and same wife for almost 38 years?"

"I suppose."

"That kind of experience and faithfulness are hard to find. You know the Bible, you've been used in ministry in many different capacities, and you love to tell stories. Why don't you write? Ask God to show you, I'll bet you can start this new chapter in life by writing a unique story that people would want to read."

"Like what?"

"Like me!"

"Like you?"

"Tom, tell everyone our story."

"But people would never believe me."

"Maybe not; but it's a great story. Tell it. The story isn't about me, it's about you and God!"

"Maybe you're right, Sonny, but where do I begin?"

"You need to first begin with God: what scripture has He been using lately to speak to you?"

"Well, Sonny, I've really been meditating on Psalm 92. Remember when God showed me how to answer Bubby's questions?"

"Have you been meditating on the last four verses? I think those are for you, especially now. Get your Bible out."

I ran in the house and picked up my torn and tattered Bible that I have been using for years and turned to Psalm 92:12-15:

> The righteous shall flourish like a palm tree. He shall grow like a cedar in Lebanon. Those who are planted in the house of the Lord shall flourish in the courts of our God. They shall still bear fruit in old age; they shall be fresh and flourishing, to declare that the Lord is upright: He is my rock, and there is no unrighteousness in Him.

"Tom, because of God, you're a righteous man. If your motive is to declare that the Lord is upright, that He's your rock, and it's all about His righteousness, you'll be fine. I don't think you're old, Tom, but unfortunately society may. I'm confident you'll bear fruit in whatever God has for you, maybe now more than ever."

I was feeling thoroughly encouraged, "Thank you, Sonny. You have a great way of putting things into perspective. I wish our time together wouldn't have to end."

"Tom, when this adventure is over, you will have much to write about. No matter what my fate, when it's time to meet my bride, you should be rejoicing with me."

"I'm almost there, my dear Son of Mantis. I'm almost there."

So, Sonny and I prayed for our miracle to continue, for God's leading and His will to be done for both of us. With unwavering faith, we believed God would complete that which He had begun.

WE BECOME WHAT
WE BEHOLD

Crystal had just arrived home after spending the afternoon in prayer with her lady's prayer group at church. I wished I could tell her about what Sonny and I had prayed, but I realized it was not the time. If I were to write about our experiences, I know it would be an amazing story about God more than Sonny or myself, so I just laid it down for the time being, took a few journal notes, and greeted my precious bride. "How was your afternoon, Sweetheart. How are your lady friends?"

Crystal smiled, almost laughing, "They're doing really well. We enjoyed lunch together, had an intense prayer time, and then just reminisced. It was really fun."

"Reminisced? About what?"

"We were talking about the television programs we watched as children and how different TV and entertainment are today. You know, when we were young, there weren't as many options or distractions; we didn't have the internet. Life seemed much simpler."

I nodded, "We're pulled in so many directions. Faith and her friends are living among the social media generation of YouTube, and Twitter; social media is everything. And everyone has an immediate opinion."

"And any opinion masquerades as truth. People don't take the time to read and study. Unless you read the Bible and believe it, anything goes."

"Crystal, look what I journaled this morning. I was reading Matthew 24: 'And Jesus answered and said to them: Take heed that no one deceives you.'"

"That's what we were talking about today; it seems like deception has crept in everywhere."

"Unless we pursue God, we can be easily deceived."

"Brenda brought up 2 Corinthians 3:18: 'We with unveiled faces beholding the glory of the Lord, are being transformed into the same image from one degree of glory to the other.' So, if we're spending time in prayer, Bible Study, worship, and ministry, we can understand truth, and it just increases. But if we're on our phone or computer all day with social media or entertainment, we can become something very different."

"We become what we behold. When I was a little kid, you know, I loved Roy Rogers. He was my cowboy hero, so I listened to his records, watched his TV show, wore cowboy boots, wore the hat and holster, and talked about the things he had on his show. I became a mini-Roy Rogers. I named my pet turtle, Roy, and when the girls were young, we had a tortoise, do you remember his name?"

"Trigger, same as Roy Rogers' horse. How could I forget that?"

"And with Roy, you always knew who the bad guy was. Nowadays, you can't be too sure."

"That was one of the points Brenda was making. Today good is portrayed as evil and evil portrayed as good. So tell me, as you got older, who else influenced you?"

"Of course, there were sports. Being a Pittsburgh Pirates fan, I loved Roberto Clemente. I always appreciated his baseball skill; he was an amazing all-around player. But he died in a plane crash going to help earthquake victims when I was in high school. That had a deep impact on me; the fact that he wasn't just a sports star but desired to serve others stuck with me."

"This is the kind of reminiscing we did this afternoon. I love hearing your stories. Anyone else influence you?"

"Well, I didn't realize it until much later, but my biggest hero was Mr. Rogers with his children's TV show on public television."

"Mr. Rogers? First Roy Rogers, then Fred Rogers."

"That's funny, I didn't realize that."

"I knew you liked him when the kids were growing up, especially with Heather and the twins. Do you remember when Heather and Shawna Goldstone went out to dinner with you and Mr. McFeely from the show when we lived in California? He was doing a public appearance."

"That was one of the highlights of my daddy/daughter dates with Heather. What was interesting is that David Newell, alias Mr. McFeely, was very much like Mr. Rogers. He was a good example of becoming what he beheld. He listened to the girls very intently and asked them questions just like Mr. Rogers did on the TV show. We had a great evening. But again, that was a different era where a show that dealt with children's feelings and emotions could emerge. I'm not too sure if that could happen so easily today."

"You see, that is the sort of thing that came up today. Times seemed to be much more innocent and our heroes were humble. One of the ladies brought up the idea of all these superhero movies and how these indestructible men and women have become the kids' heroes. And Suzie made a great observation about Captain America. He was an idealist, born in a different time, and he had a hard time living in a different era because everything had changed so much. Morals and ideals were different when he was fighting evil in World War II."

"You do realize Crystal that Captain America's real name is Steve Rogers. Again, we have a humble man named Rogers with a different demeanor than the others. This is really funny."

"Tom, you're not going to go out and buy a leotard, mask, and shield to become like him now, are you?"

"No, my precious bride, I'm going to go upstairs, get changed, and prepare for our Bible study. Instead of Captain America, pray that I become more like Jesus."

Crystal nodded and smiled knowing that in all the humor there was truth. As we beheld our Savior, we were being transformed into His image.

TEACH US TO PRAY

That evening was our church home group Bible study that we had a few times a month. I invited Myles and his wife, but they couldn't come. We had a small group that evening; just my family and two other couples, along with a single widow. First, we spent time in worship, and then a short Bible study.

On this particular evening, we were studying the Lord's Prayer from Matthew 6 and Luke 11. I have heard many teachings on this perfect prayer, but I never get tired of it. And of course, there was Sonny. He was such an integral part of my life over the last few weeks that I couldn't help but think of him. So early in the week, when I asked God what I should talk about, all I could picture was that praying mantis. From the onset of our encounter, he encouraged me to pray.

I desperately wanted to tell everyone that I was best friends with a praying mantis and explain to them that he didn't just appear to be praying, but that he actually did pray. I was bursting at the seams to describe our adventures, but I couldn't. So even better, I talked about Jesus and what He had to say about prayer.

A year ago, my regional manager, who also loves Jesus, suggested something to me. He recommended that I find someone to father me. Although he is 15 years younger than I, he could see something in me that still needed a touch from a father. My earthly father and I resolved many issues before he passed away several years ago, but something deep within me still needed a father's touch.

So, I sought out a very wise man who had had a lot of influence in my life through teaching. My friend, John Brown, who recently turned 80, accepted my invitation, and we spent several hours together. He listened intently to the many issues in my life, and I asked for his direction. He is a very humble man, and he felt like there wasn't much to say, but he did hand me a couple books and prayed for me.

One of the books was entitled *How to Develop a Powerful Prayer Life.* I studied it for weeks and even discussed it previously at my home group. Then when Sonny showed up, my desire to pray really heated up.

If you ask anyone if they know how to pray, most will say they do. But during my study, I recognized something new. The disciples were asking Jesus to teach them to pray. It made me realize that we need to be taught, and we need to be taught by God. John Brown can teach me, and Sonny can teach me, but until I come to God as my heavenly Father, something will be missing.

The first prayer I learned as a child was getting a fresh overhaul. I've said it thousands of times in my life, in church services, at funerals, and many other religious functions, but now I was truly coming to my Heavenly

Father with a desire to know Him and His ways. Let's repeat it together. Let's say it in the same version that I learned as a child:

> Our Father who art in Heaven, hallowed be Thy name,
>
> Thy Kingdom come, thy will be done, on earth as it is in Heaven.
>
> Give us this day, our daily bread, and forgive us our trespasses,
>
> As we forgive those who trespass against us,
>
> And lead us not into temptation but deliver us from evil.

This is how it is written in Luke 11 when Jesus' disciples asked Him to teach them to pray. Then in Matthew 6, it is the same except for the summarizing addition of, "for Thine is the kingdom and the power and the glory. Amen."

Jesus was teaching us to first go to the source that He lived from and the only source that could answer every need. This source was not just His Father but "our" Father. Our earthly fathers are limited, but our Heavenly Father can give us access to a Kingdom which is unlike the world that we live in, where any need can be satisfied when we come to this Father. Now what else could we ask for?

As we completed our Bible study that evening, we all prayed to "Our Father," and we all experienced a bit of heaven. We asked him to meet needs: spiritual, emotional, and physical. We asked for forgiveness and were able to forgive. We asked him to gird our emotions so we would not be tempted into self-destructive behavior. And we asked for his protection and guidance.

After everyone went home that evening, I went out on the back deck to get a breath of fresh air. The weather was beginning to get cooler and I remembered that my time with Sonny was running out. It was the first time that thought came up when I didn't feel anxious. A passage popped into my mind from Philippians 4:6-7: "Be anxious for nothing, but in everything by prayer and supplication, with thanksgiving, let your requests be made known to God; and the peace of God, which surpasses all understanding will guard your heart and minds through Christ Jesus."

"Heavenly Father, thank You for teaching me how to come to You and depend on You, trusting that You will meet every need. Now help me be a blessing to Sonny, and over the next few days, show me how to be as good a friend to him as he has been to me. Thank You, Father. I ask this in Your Son Jesus' holy name. Amen."

SEVEN TIMES
SEVENTY

Saturday mornings are my favorite. No matter what has occurred during the previous five days, I get a rest from the daily grind for two whole days. But this day was extra special. I felt that God had given me an idea to help Sonny, and I couldn't wait to tell him.

I went out back and scanned my backyard. Usually he sought me out if he was close by, so I patiently walked around expecting Sonny's surprise entrance. However, after waiting and praying for several minutes, there was no Son of Mantis, so I sat down and opened my Bible.

I turned to Matthew 6 and was reminded of how we had prayed in the home group. One of the women had us pray for her shoulder that was frozen. Before we prayed, she told us how she needed to forgive someone. She prayed a beautiful prayer of forgiveness and then asked for God to touch her shoulder. We all agreed, and she immediately had more mobility; God was working in this precious friend.

I have come to appreciate how emphatic Jesus is concerning forgiveness. Right after His instruction concerning prayer in Matthew 6:14, Jesus made a statement that I have found to be one of the key dictates for a healthy life, "For if you forgive men their trespasses, your heavenly Father will also forgive you. But if you do not forgive men their trespasses, neither will your Father forgive your trespasses."

Then in Mark 11, Jesus challenged His disciples to pray with faith believing that their prayers would be answered,

> "Have faith in God. For assuredly, I say to you, whoever says to this mountain, 'Be removed and be cast into the sea,' and does not doubt in his heart, but believe that those things he says will be done, he will have whatever he says."

And once again He linked forgiveness to prayer:

> "And whenever you stand praying, if you have anything against anyone, forgive him, that your Father in heaven may also forgive your trespasses. But if you do not forgive, neither will your Father in heaven forgive your trespasses" (Mark 11:22-25).

Do you think God really wants us to grasp this? In Matthew 18, Jesus continued to teach on prayer, but I couldn't help but notice how His disciples again began asking about forgiveness. Peter asked, "Lord, how often shall my brother sin against me, and I forgive him? Up to seven times? Jesus said to him, "I do not say to you up to seven times, but up to seventy times seven."

Then He told a parable that would blow them away. He described a wicked servant who is forgiven an insurmountable debt, owing his master more money than he could ever repay. Then the servant goes out and demands payment of a small debt from a fellow servant and throws him in jail when he can't pay.

The master finds out and we read the following in verses 34 and 35: "And his master was angry and delivered him to the torturers until he could pay all that was due him. So, my Heavenly Father also will do to you if each of you, from his heart, does not forgive his brother his trespasses."

I don't know about you, but I want my heavenly Father to forgive me. I am not 100% sure what it means to be "delivered to the torturers," but whether that is for eternity or while on this earth, it does not sound appealing. Do you think that many of our sorrows, our aches and pains could be caused by our unforgiveness?

Healing, prayer, and forgiveness are obviously related. In James 5, he instructed people who are sick to go to the elders of the church and have them anoint with oil and pray in faith for their healing. Verses 15 and 16 say, "And the prayer of faith will save the sick, and the Lord will raise him up. And if he has committed sins, he will be forgiven. Confess your trespasses to one another, and pray for one another, that you may be healed. The effective fervent prayer of a righteous man avails much."

This led me to an intimate time of prayer cleansing my heart before the Lord. As I concluded, I closed my eyes and prayed out loud, "Show me, Lord, if there is any wicked way in me. I want to be a righteous man."

I heard a voice, "You've neglected your praying mantis friend; he's hungry and needs sustenance!"

I opened my eyes to see Sonny looking up at me

standing in the middle of my Bible. I shook my head, "So, when did you start answering for God?"

"I thought it wouldn't hurt just this once."

"Alright, I've been studying prayer and forgiveness. So, I forgive you for impersonating God."

"Thanks. Besides, I think God's voice may have a little more bass tone to it. Don't you think?"

"Perhaps."

"Now, Tom, I want to get serious. There's a problem. Your yard is running out of sustenance. Just a couple of days ago, there were mosquitos, flies, bees, and various other delicacies, but this cooler weather is changing that. My bride's still here, and she's better at catching prey than I, but we may need to be moving on, or maybe it's time we meet. She has been giving me hints, looking back for me. I think it's almost time. But if there's not enough food here, she may want to move on."

"Sonny, I have a solution. When praying last night, after my home group Bible study. I had an idea I believe you'll like. I believe your bride will like it, too."

"Really, you aren't going to try to talk to her again, are you?"

"No. Sonny, but I thought I could help you and your bride with the perfect setting to make disciples. I want to take you to the Chateau Elan."

"Really, you would do that for me? But wait, how will you get us there? She isn't just going to hop in your car like I would. She has no desire to listen to you. What are you going to do?"

"I'm not sure, but I'll pray. I'll trust God and pray, and He'll show me what to do."

"Alright righteous man, it's time to be effective and fervent. Go for it!"

Sonny and I prayed together that I would get a

creative idea to make this happen. It reminded me of our first encounter when Sonny was teaching me how to wait on God. I was confident that the answer would come. I had faith that we could move mountains.

26

THE ESCAPE PLAN

After church the next day, instead of eating out with friends, I decided to plan how I was going to get Sonny and his bride into my car and transfer them to the Chateau Elan. I had prayed quite a bit on this and had come up with the conclusion, but it would have to be supernatural. I had no clue how to get them both into my car willingly.

I was starving, so when I came home, I immediately turned on the oven and baked two frozen cauliflower crusted pizzas and made a salad. As I opened the bag of salad and poured it in the bowl, out came a live insect, some type of caterpillar. I thought to myself, *If only Sonny was here, we could all enjoy lunch together.*

Then it hit me. The only thing that motivated Sonny and his bride was live food. If I could fill my car with delectable creepy crawlies, then they couldn't resist. The idea disgusted me. I was never all that excited about insects in food or crawling anywhere near me for that matter. But now I was considering loading my van with live insects to attract a praying mantis that wanted nothing to do with me.

The King James version of the Bible calls us a "peculiar people." I was beginning to believe that applied to me. "Lord, how am I going to get live insects into my van, and then lead Sonny and his bride to hop in. I need help. I can't do this alone. I know Sonny will help, but even he can't dictate what his bride will do. Help me figure this out."

I finished my pizza as I thought it out, and I left the remainder on plates in the kitchen for when the girls got back from church. They had taken Faith's car because they also had to run some errands. I began to look around outside the house and inside the garage wondering if the idea would just pop into my mind.

I went onto the back deck, walked around the house, and then inspected the garage until I saw several things that intrigued me. Inside the garage was a mesh material that we used to cover the tomatoes so birds and other critters couldn't eat them. Then I realized that the area with the most insects was the pots of plants on the deck. How in the world could I get enough plants in my car, enough insects to attract the bride, and a mesh between me and them so I didn't have a bunch of insects flying or crawling in my face while driving?

With this general idea in mind, I began to look where any modern 21st century person would go to get such information — the internet. I knew someone had to have done something like this previously and I could just imitate him. I looked on several different web sites but couldn't find an example of someone trying to lure a mantis into their vehicle. Then it dawned on me that I was probably the only person on the face of our planet who would try such a thing.

However, I did get some tips. The best advice I read was to attract them with water, ground cover, and fragrant, colorful plants. Well, we had an abundance of all the above, so I began to plan my van makeover. I was about to transform the van into a mantis reserve, part terrarium and part zoo. I would take out the middle seats of the van, fill the middle with plants, put a planter in the middle with a water tray, place some ground cover plants that had flowers in the middle, and some other colorful, fragrant plants. I would put the mesh between me and the middle to protect me, and add an array of beetles, crickets, grasshoppers, moths, mice, tree frogs, and hummingbirds.

Easy peasy, right? Wrong! Where in the world would I get a supply of these creatures and place them in the van quick enough to avoid their escape, while luring the bride? This idea was becoming more ridiculous with every new thought, "Lord, is this what You want me to do?"

I prayed for several minutes hoping that I would get some better or easier idea. Then it hit me; I needed to run this by Sonny and ask what he thought. Maybe he could shape this into the direction it needed to go. I sat out on the back deck, searching the area for Sonny or his bride to no avail. I descended the deck steps into the backyard and there he was: Sonny was underneath the rosemary bush, but as I got closer, I knew something was wrong. I got closer and saw a skeleton of a mantis. I got closer and put my face right up to it, "Sonny, is that you? Have you been eaten, and this is all that's left?"

"I sure hope not! Who are you talking to, Tom?"

I turned to the left and saw him on the planter a few feet away. I couldn't help but exclaim, "Sonny, what is this skeleton? I got scared it was you!"

"Really, Tom, I thought you read all about the mantis. That was my bride's last molt. That is her last exoskeleton from a couple weeks ago. We mantis molt or shed our skin between seven and nine times until adulthood. That thing should have blown away and turned to dust by now, but I suppose it was protected underneath that plant."

"I do remember something about molting in my study, but I was looking for you, and didn't expect that."

"So, what have you come up with? It's almost time to meet my bride. Maybe even today."

"No, no you can't. I mean, I guess you can, but I wanted to do this for you. I want to take you to the Chateau Elan. It has a golf course and vineyard and lots of room for your offspring to be born and have a good chance of surviving and thriving in the fields with the insects and the critters."

"Tom, that's appreciated, but I've been following my bride for the last few weeks and I can sense that this is our time. Can you take us now?"

"Now, but what about my plan? How am I going to get her into my van? You even asked that question the other day."

"You're right Tom, but you know what, I'm ready to meet her. And she's right there on the New Guinea Impatiens that's below the big bird feeder and the bird bath in the middle of the yard. At this point in our courtship, there are just two steps left. I do my fancy dance, and then I approach her to make disciples. Then, as we make disciples, I find out if she needs more protein or if I survive a little longer. Either way, I'm ready. This is how God designed me, I'm ready to do God's will and produce the next generation."

"But how do we get her in the van? You said it yourself. She won't follow or communicate with me."

"We will kidnap her!"

"Kidnap her? Really, that doesn't sound right. That doesn't sound like the right setting for you to meet your bride!"

"Well, maybe kidnap is too strong a word. She has captured my heart and it's time for us to capture her and take her to the vineyard."

"How?"

"Look in the garage. Crystal picks up all kinds of things at thrift stores and sells them. See if you can find a temporary shelter where my bride could dwell for the next hour."

I went into the garage and looked around. There were all kinds of purses and buckets and planters, but nothing big enough to capture the bride safely. Then, I got closer to the garage door and saw a pile of stuff Crystal just picked up. There it was — a little pet carrier people use on airplanes to keep their small pets while traveling. I swooped it up and brought it out to show Sonny.

Now where was he? He wasn't where I left him, "Sonny where are you? I found the perfect travel container."

In more of a whisper, I heard Sonny call me forth, "Over here Tom, just below my bride, she got a grasshopper and still has a way to go. If we capture her while eating, she may not notice."

The travel container had plenty of room and a mesh outer cover to provide ventilation. I grabbed a couple plant parts and threw them in to make her at home. I looked down at Sonny and said a prayer, "Lord, help this work. You know what needs to happen here."

Sonny's bride happened to be atop the New Guinea Impatiens with nothing around her. It was the perfect position to capture her. I opened one end holding the flap up with one hand, then swiftly, in one single motion scooped up Sonny's bride. I slowly knelt to the ground so as not to injure her while I zipped the open end shut, and there it was: mantis bride In a box!

Sonny flew up on my shoulder as I slowly got up carrying his bride who was still munching the grasshopper amongst the flowers in the container. I reached in my pocket for the car keys and we went into the garage.

I gently placed the container down between the middle seats and watched his bride continue to munch away. The transfer was a success. Sonny was still on my shoulder looking down in adoration. I opened the garage door and backed out of the driveway.

We were on our way. I looked at Sonny who was transfixed on the container, "Well, Sonny, it takes a little more than an hour to get there. I guess this is our last hour together." He just looked at me with those big eyes and smiled, then looked back down at his bride.

27

SPEECHLESS

As I backed out and turned to head out with these two lovebirds, or should I say lovebird eaters, Faith drove up with Crystal. I wanted to drive off without acknowledging them, but it was too late. Crystal got out of the car before they went up the driveway. Sonny jumped down to be beside his bride and avoid a confrontation with Crystal.

She ran up to the window and motioned to put it down, "Tom, I'm sorry it took so long to get home, but where are you going? Aren't we going to eat?"

"I already ate. You go ahead and eat with Faith; I will be back in a couple of hours."

"Couple of hours, it's Sunday, I want to be with you. I had a big breakfast; I can wait to eat. Let me tell Faith, and I'll be right back."

She ran up and explained to Faith and came running back to the car. My mind was staggered with all types of thoughts. What was I about to tell Crystal?

She opened the door with wide eyes, "Where are you going?"

"To the Chateau Elan."

"What, that's over an hour away. Why in the world would you need to go out there?"

"It's a long story."

"We have an hour."

"True, well . . ."

I looked down at Sonny. He was looking back at me as if he was about to burst out laughing, I wasn't sure how to continue, but I did, "Well, do you remember that praying mantis we saw a few weeks ago? Well, I'm taking him to the Chateau Elan for his honeymoon."

"Tom, what are you talking about? We saw that insect weeks ago. Are you still looking for him? Really, why are we going to the Chateau Elan?"

I didn't expect it, but Sonny flew up on my shoulder and smiled. Crystal screamed and the earth stood still. She stared at both of us and was speechless.

Then with the same likable voice that drew me to him, Sonny nonchalantly began to speak, "It's true Crystal. Your husband is driving me to the Chateau Elan where he will let me go into the vineyard with my bride. There she is down below in the doggy container finishing a grasshopper."

Crystal stared at me and Sonny. Then stared down at the doggy bag, then started to stutter, then finally said, "It's talking!"

"Well yes, he's talking. Crystal meet Sonny, Sonny meet Crystal."

Sonny continued, "It's a pleasure to meet you. How are you this fine afternoon?"

"Well, I was just fine, I'm not too sure right now. Are you, a praying mantis, talking to me, a human being?"

Sonny looked at me shaking his head, then looked back at Crystal, "Absolutely!"

"This can't be, this shouldn't happen. This is demonic, that little creature is possessed!"

I took over the conversation. "No, he isn't Crystal. Jesus said, 'A house divided cannot stand.' This little fellow has done nothing but show me the grace of our Savior, and the love of Father God. Sonny is a miracle. Now take a deep breath and calm down. This is Sonny, or more formally, Son of Mantis. God has allowed Sonny to communicate with me since we met and has done much to get me back on track with the Lord. He has helped me handle the stress at work and helped me uncover some forgotten things in my heart. Sonny has been a great friend when I needed one. Now, I'm being a friend to him and his bride. I'm taking them to a perfect setting so they can create the next generation of mantises and spend their last days."

Sonny added, "Look around you. Everything the Lord created speaks of Him, so I speak of Him. Your husband's a praying man, and I'm a praying mantis. God's ways are not our ways, just listen, and we'll tell you the whole story."

For the next half hour, Sonny and I described our adventure. We laughed and cried, and Crystal did the same. By the time we were done, Crystal was talking too, "Tom, I don't know what to say except this is amazing, and cool, and weird, and a lot of things, but I'm glad I'm in on it now."

Then Crystal's eyes got big, and she shouted, "Stop the van, Tom. Turn around."

I was confused, "What? Why?"

"Tom, I just thought of something that you would never think of because you aren't a gardener. Pull off this exit." I have learned to trust my wife when she is adamant, so I pulled off the exit and we stopped in the parking lot of a church.

Crystal looked at me with sorrowful puppy eyes, and gently explained, "I would love to go with you and spend a romantic weekend at the Chateau Elan and tour the vineyard and maybe let you play a round of golf. It's an amazing place. But it's for people, and people don't like insects. That vineyard and that golf course will be sprayed with all kinds of pesticides and insecticides. If you love Sonny and his bride, you won't take them there."

I looked at Sonny, Sonny looked at me, and we both grunted with wide eyes, "Ugh!"

I talked first, "Sonny, I'm so sorry, I never thought of that. No wonder I was having so much trouble planning this escape. God didn't want the escape, but I got caught up in my plan. Crystal saved your lives, Sonny, and the lives of the next generation."

Sonny sighed and responded, "Tom, God brought Crystal into this car. Thank you, Crystal. Tom has one smart bride!"

Crystal looked down at Sonny, "You're so welcome, Sonny, and thank you. You must be one of the reasons that I haven't used any insecticides for the last month or so. Between you and the ladybugs, I haven't seen any unwanted insects, so I haven't sprayed."

I interrupted, "Hey, let's get back on the Interstate and get back home, I think we need to prepare some room in our backyard for many-a-mantis next spring."

I looked up at the cross on the steeple of the church we were near and smiled with a deep sense of gratitude, then proceeded to the Interstate. I was going in the opposite direction on our way home, and I could see Crystal was very comfortable talking to Sonny now. I was wondering when Crystal would ask, "Sonny, I just have one question. Does your bride speak too?"

We looked down at Sonny's bride. She had finished her grasshopper by now and she looked up through the carrier. She obviously looked at Crystal and then turned to look at Sonny who had just hopped back on my shoulder. She just blinked.

Sonny explained, "My bride hasn't opened her mouth to utter a word, but look at those eyes, isn't she wonderful?"

With that, Sonny leaped down beside her. He just stared and was mesmerized with his bride. Crystal and I laughed and talked about how hard it was to keep all this a secret.

"Tom, I can understand you not knowing how to talk about this, but no more insect secrets, okay?"

"Okay, my precious bride!'

As we were getting off our Interstate exit and almost home, we looked down at Sonny to see that he started swaying. Then he started shaking, then he started twirling.

Crystal whispered, "What's he doing? Is he dancing?"

"That must be his fancy dance: It's time to do his fancy dance."

I focused on my driving, but Crystal watched intently. Crystal was beginning to understand.

I thought of a worship song we sang in church recently based on the Song of Solomon. I took Crystal by the hand, "Let's help him with a song, do you remember this?"

Dance with me, O Lover of my soul — to the song of all songs

Romance me, O Lover of my soul — to the song of all songs

Behold, you have come, over the hills, upon the mountains

To me you have run, my beloved, you've captured my heart

(©Integrity Music, used with permission)

As we sang, Sonny danced to the music. His feelers would reach out as his bride's feelers reached out through the carrier. Sonny continued his fancy dance as we drove up our driveway. We would soon release this couple back to our pesticide-free backyard.

28

A FOND FAREWELL

The garage door opened and Crystal looked at me with great empathy, seeing the emotion in my eyes. I didn't feel like talking. I was happy for Sonny, but sad I had to say goodbye. I looked down as Sonny concluded his fancy dance for now. He looked up at me as I sighed and took a deep breath, "Sonny, jump up on my shoulder and I'll take you two to the perfect place in our backyard. It will give you privacy and you can meet your bride as God intended."

He hopped up and I reached back for the pet carrier. Sonny's bride did not put up a fight as I lifted the container and proceeded out of the car. I went out the side garage door and through the open gate where it had fallen just weeks ago. As we searched the backyard, there were many possibilities.

Everything around our backyard reminded me of the times with Sonny: the St. Francis statue, the hummingbird feeder, rosemary bush, the back deck, the plethora of New Guinea Impatiens, begonias, Persian Shields, and other plants. I wanted to pick the perfect spot where they could have their privacy and hope that no other animal happened to find them while they met.

Then I went over to our gate with Psalm 24:7 painted on it. *Maybe they can go behind the gate.* No, the ivy was too tall and looked foreboding. Who knows what lurked among the ivy? I once saw an opossum slink through there. I did not want them to suffer the wrath of another critter.

Sonny hopped on top of the carrier as his antennae were reaching down for his bride. I needed to find something fast. Then I looked down and fifteen feet to the right of the painted gate, a little closer to the house, was an oval patch of deep monkey grass and plants surrounded by bushes, an island of sorts, right in front of the only maple tree in our yard. It was the perfect place not near a bird feeder or critter lair, and best of all it had an elevated hotel for our couple. In the middle of this island was a red Radio Flyer wagon that my wife placed as a planter for various ferns and other plants. It was the perfect, safe setting for our couple to begin the next generation.

I knelt in front of the Flyer and began to unzip the carrier flap, but then I thought of something. It would be best if we had some food for the bride so she wouldn't consider Sonny her only option. Was I ever glad that the fence was down. My neighbor, Myles, had a can of worms in his backyard he kept for fishing.

"Sonny, I'm going next door and grab some live worms. Here, look at your honeymoon suite. What do you think?"

"It's perfect, Tom; put us down in there and go get the worms, I need to finish my fancy dance."

I placed his bride on the edge of the Radio Flyer in

the carrier and Sonny amongst the ferns; he once again began his fancy dance as I ran back to Myles' house. Right beside his porch was the can. I looked in and saw a favorable collection: worms of different sizes, and even some beetles mixed in black soil.

As I was running back into my yard, Crystal was cautiously coming out our back door looking for me and our mantis friends. I waved at Crystal and motioned for her to follow me, "Come here, darling, I found the perfect honeymoon spot. Sonny's finishing his fancy dance and

I'm getting some live lunch for his bride to distract her from devouring him."

Crystal followed me as I knelt and slowly removed our bride from the carrier. I placed her on a leaf and put the container aside. I handed the can to Crystal and asked, "Can you come down here and hold the can while I pull out a worm or two?"

Crystal knelt beside me and I rummaged for the perfect worms. As we fumbled with the bait, we weren't watching the mantis couple. When we looked back, Sonny was slowly approaching his bride from behind. If she was hungry and saw Sonny, they may not have the chance to make disciples.

Suddenly, our female turned around as I pulled out a worm and dangled the wiggler in front of her. She looked at Sonny but attacked the worm instead, almost attacking my fingers at the same time. Crystal and I flinched back a bit as I frantically grabbed a chunk of dirt with several creepy crawlies, including some beetles, and placed them in front of the bride. Crystal and I got up and took a few steps back.

My wife took me by the hand and nudged me, "Come on, Cupid, it's time to let nature take its course. I'm so blessed to be your wife. You did everything possible to help your friend, and now he's on his own."

I knelt once more and watched as Sonny approached his bride. He took one look back, just like the first time we saw him. Surprisingly, he acknowledged me: "Good-bye, Neighbor. I can handle it from here. When you see all my disciples running around next spring, I want you to remember this one thing: God is good. When you write about our adventure, remember that God is good."

I got up with a tear in my eye and took Crystal by

the hand. I didn't look back; it was Sonny's time to finally meet his bride as God intended. As we walked into the house, Crystal and I rejoiced with song:

I love you, Lord, oh, your mercy never fails me

All my days, I've been held in your hands

From the moment that I wake up until I lay my head,

I will sing of the goodness of God

All my life you have been faithful, all my life you have been so, so good

With every breath that I am able, I will sing of the goodness of God

I love your voice. You have lead me through the fire.

In darkest nights you are close like no other

I've known you as a father, I've known you as a friend

And I have lived in the goodness of God!

(©Bethel Music Publishing, ©Essential Music Publishing, ©Capitol CMG Publishing, used by permission)

CONCLUSION

Autumn progressed and the weather cooled quite a bit. I stopped looking for Sonny; I knew if he was still around, we'd meet again. I found the bride's ootheca or egg case hidden on a branch in a bush, so I was sure of their meeting. I have been praying for its protection daily. Spring will be here before we know it.

So, I took Sonny's advice and wrote our story. It really is more about God than me or Sonny. God was looking for me, and he used Sonny to call me out. He is calling all of us out of our "less than" treadmill lifestyle into a life of trust and dependence, no matter what we have been through in the past or are going through at the moment. It is the kind of trust and dependence that doesn't only help with our difficulties but creates an adventure. Isn't that we want? I want adventure; I want fulfillment. No matter how old or young, our Creator calls us to more. Are you ready for "more"?

When our God finished creating the heavens and the earth, he culminated his creation with mankind. Genesis 1:31 states, "Then God saw everything that He had made, and indeed it was very good." He wants us to know that He is good, but He also wants us to know that a life yoked to Him is "very good."

We are His precious bride, and I am so thankful; I could have missed that; but I didn't. How about you?

Jesus said, "The time is fulfilled and the kingdom of God is at hand. Repent and believe in the gospel."

My prayer for you is from Ephesians 3:17-19:

That Christ may dwell in your hearts through faith; that you, being rooted and grounded in love, may be able to comprehend with all the saints what is the width and length and dept and height — to know the love of Christ which passes knowledge; that you may be filled with all the fullness of God.

EPILOGUE

Obviously, this book is fiction, but it is also filled with some of my most God-filled true-life experiences. For me, the weaving of these two was a necessary task. God knew that both the fictional and non-fictional Tom Borga needed help to re-focus, so He sent Sonny.

When I began writing this story, I had no idea that God would be transitioning me to a life outside of my 38-year sales career. As the fictional Tom wondered about his future, the non-fictional Tom did the same. As Sonny helped the fictional Tom with some ideas for his future, the non-fictional Tom was praying.

I was praying that I would be able to retire from lighting sales earlier than expected. I was having a tough year in sales, and after 38 years, I was stressed by the demands. When I asked God if He might have something different for me, I felt like He asked me a question, "What else can you do, Tom?" My reply came pretty fast, "I can communicate, God. I'm a communicator."

Then Sonny arrived.

The idea for Sonny started out as the original photo that you saw at the beginning of the book. Crystal called me out to see the mantis and took that photo; it was very much like our first chapter. And as I looked at that picture day after day, it became an obsession for me. I knew God wanted me to tell Sonny's story, but I wasn't sure how to do it. Then, I started learning facts about the praying mantis and I became more fascinated; I had no choice. I had to write this.

I realized that the best story is always the story

you know best, aka your own life. Thus, I adopted the idea to include many of my real-life moments, surrounded by Sonny's guidance and friendship. It seemed to be a perfect combination of truth and fiction, telling Sonny's story while at the same time leaving my children and grandchildren with a factual account of God's goodness in my life.

All the people I included in this book are real friends, family, or people I have worked with, including real customers. I did change a few names to protect the innocent or for literary continuity and blended experiences that I had with several people into one to create a cohesive timeframe or story line.

So, you may want to know if my company put me out to pasture. The answer is no — with a caveat. Our world situation with COVID-19 created the perfect storm where 59% of my business, the retail segment, stopped ordering completely for three months and some customers went out of business. My company was thoughtful and came up with a program to give the salespeople double commissions and new products to help us survive.

But as I wondered about my future, the owners came to me first. I had a candid conversation where they graciously gave me the opportunity to leave early and helped me work out the financial means by which I could do that. God answered my prayer. While Sonny and Tom had their fictional adventure, I was having my real-life adventure.

I wrote this mostly during our COVID-19 experience, and at the time of this writing, it is still an ongoing saga. I toyed with the idea of including issues concerning the pandemic into the story but knew it would take over the story rather than add to it, so I dismissed the idea. But the great thing about a God-story is that it is always applicable. So many of the things I was writing helped me focus on His promises rather than our uncertain times.

Another true situation described in these pages developed into a precious conclusion: You may want to know how things turned out with 93-year-old Bubby. Certainly, I cannot adequately explain all the nuances of God dealing with evil in our world. However, I did come back to Bubby with what I concluded to be God's answer about Hitler from Psalm 92.

She listened and was silent, and I could tell she was thinking. She was still sharp, so she weighed our words and pondered the scripture. I am not sure how much of an impact that had on her, but a few months later, she became very ill, and many loved ones shared God's truth with her repeatedly.

Then, in perfect harmony with God's timing, this old Jewish woman, only a few days before her passing, came to know the love of God through Jesus Christ as her Messiah. Milton and Leady Mendoza, who lived with her, had the pleasure of leading Bubby to truth's doorway so she could step in. God isn't so concerned with how we get saved, just that we get saved. Whether we come to Him at the eleventh hour like Bubby, or early in life, trusting in Jesus and understanding His love is a must.

Jesus said, "I am the way, the truth, and the life, no man comes to the Father, but by me" (John 14:6). If you are not too sure what that means, give me a call. I'd be glad to tell you more. Don't wait until you are 93. Ask God to forgive you and cleanse you now. He is as close as Sonny's whisper, "Hi neighbor, can I help you?"

As I prepared to leave a 38-year sales career, I completed this book. I believe that God's grace at selling light bulbs can continue through anything He has for my future.

Whether I write anything after this or not, I know God has my future in His hands, and I thank you for reading what I believe God gave me.

In the meantime, "Look up, your redemption draws near." If you do, an adventure is promised to you also.

Sample prayer to begin a life with God:

Lord, I surrender everything to You: my will, all rights, and all control. I ask You to forgive me. I repent for believing I could control everything and everyone in my life, and I ask You to forgive all my sins, all the lies, manipulations, and blatant rebellious activity that is contrary to Your Word. Come into my life and rule me from head to toe, inside and out, everything about me. Fill me with Your Spirit and show me how to live this out. I thank You for Your sacrifice for me on the cross. I pray this in the name of Jesus Christ. Amen.

SPECIAL ACKNOWLEDGEMENTS

First of all, thank you John Stanko for helping me sandpaper the rough edges of this story. I didn't know I needed help—funny thing!

Because everything in this book is a culmination of not just my working life, but also genuinely my lifetime, I would be remiss if I did not acknowledge those around me who have supported me all along.

My birth family was awesome; I was raised in a loving happy home. Mom nurtured and taught me how to laugh and cry; Dad exemplified hard work, and an ornery sense of humor. Though you have been gone for years, I thank you, Joe and Jean.

My sisters, Susan and her husband Umberto, Nancy Jo and her husband Paul, and Janice and her husband Doug, have always supported anything I've done and shown me much love and care. My nephews Greg, Damian, Jason, Matthew, T.J., and Adam and my niece, Gina, and their families have always been a blessing. Thank you all for wonderful family times and memories.

And my deepest gratitude to the following:

My friends growing up on "The Terrace;" you know who you are. You shaped my sense of humor and competitive spirit. Thank you.

Thank you, Kevin, Pooky, and Alan for helping me through those early years in California.

All of those who have discipled me: Paul and Grandpa Wynn, Pastor Jack, Pastor Mark, Pastor Jason and Pastor Gary, All of the teachers at TCA, Fred, Monty and Hugh, Thurman, and all my "Guy's Night" guys, and the countless others in the body of Christ who have helped me go forward with Jesus.

Thank you, John Brown, for your foundational teaching on "the Kingdom of God".

To all my co-workers and employers at Regency Lighting over 38 plus years, thank you. I enjoyed all the love and hard work, the camaraderie, and commitment to excellence. All the prayers for me have been felt. I worked with hundreds of people over all those years. I thank all of you for making that time a pleasure. A special thanks to Mike and Ron for their prayers, love, and support for so long.

And a very special thanks to Mike and Deb for your support of me and my family in more ways than I can possibly remember. I love you dearly.

My "Guys Night" friends — Matt, Todd, Greg, David H., David P., Hayes, and Jeff. Thank you for the laughter, tears, dish washing, amazing food, disagreements, prayers, and generosity. And since he is expecting it, a special thanks to Hayes for bugging me to "write your chapter" every week.

To my beautiful, talented and precious bride, Crystal, who endured being a writer's widow many a day. Thank you for your love and patience.

To my awesome daughters who put up with my humor and have taught me more than I could ever teach them. Thank you, Amber, Alicia, and Faith for your love. And to the memory of your sister, Heather, who would have really gotten a kick out of this book. And to your sister, Christina, and her family. Christina, although we didn't adopt you formally, we did emotionally; thank you, Christina for so much love over the years. If it wasn't for you, we may have never found the twins when they were in a foster home over 30 years ago.

And thank you, my grandchildren. I love you dearly and enjoy every moment I spend with you in person or in talking to you over the phone: Marina, Makayla, Conner, Thomas, Colton, Christopher, Nathaniel, Grayson, Thoryn, Harlan, and Abigail (listed from oldest to youngest), and any that may follow. Being the next generation, I pray that you would have a deep desire to know and love God as fervently or more so than your "Pop Pop." I pray for this every day.

Thank you Dean and Suzie, Frank and Priscilla, and Eric and Jonni. You three couples have blessed us in so many ways.

Thank you all who have prayed with me and for me my whole life, and my many prayer partners: Dick and Sheryl, Tim B., Monte, Greg, and the Regency prayer warriors, Chris Mc., Patrick and Christopher S. who have kept me interested in storytelling, and all my home group brothers and sisters, along with my neighbors, Zach and Myles, who can walk and pray at the same time. Then there are the old friends, John M. and John K., who I have prayed with countless times. I can never thank people enough for praying; its effectiveness should never be doubted. If I have forgotten anyone, please forgive me.

May the grace of the Lord Jesus Christ, the love of Father God, and the communion of the Holy Spirit be with you all.

You can contact me at:
tomborga@gmail.com

ABOUT TOM BORGA

I grew up in a lower middle-class neighborhood in Western, PA. Dad was a steel worker and Mom was a housewife who worked in a market across the street. I was always interested in writing stories and acting, so I went to Penn State University, graduating as a theatre arts major in 1978. I moved from PA to CA in 1979 to pursue an acting career, but got sidetracked by love. When you are young and decide to get married, sooner or later you must pursue a career, so I began selling attic insulation in Los Angeles in 1982 and then lighting products the following year. I figured it would last a short time until I could get settled and work on my acting. Now, more than 38 years later, I retired from that sales career. I have no plans to go back to acting (most likely), but the story writing has continued.

I had a dramatic conversion in 1980 and realized when I got married in 1983 to my precious bride, Crystal, that I wanted everything God wanted for me, and nothing less. For me, the acting was less, but God promised that I would use my gifts for His glory, and so I have ever since.

God brought our niece, Heather, into our home a year after we were married. We adopted her a year after that and our family tree took root. Several years later we adopted her half-sisters — the twins, Amber and Alicia. It was many years later in 1996 that our only birth child, Faith, was born. After all these years, we currently have 11 grandchildren.

I was a servant/leader at The Church On The Way in Van Nuys, CA for many years. Under the pastoral leadership of Jack Hayford, I was discipled and grew up in many ways. I began a drama ministry for children called "The Children of Light," and for more than a decade wrote, produced, and directed short plays and ministry segments for special services and church projects. Although it was never published, I wrote a full-length children's musical in 1990 that was produced at the church called *The Treasure Hunt*; the music for the play was written by Roger Thrower, currently a pastor in WV. During those years, I wrote dozens of short scripts and skits for various events. I also ministered to teens and single adults through drama and Bible studies. I assisted the singles pastor for a short time teaching and leading small groups for single Christians.

During this time, I wrote a devotional for a Christian little league for one season and was published in a fireworks magazine with a story about how I was healed of the fear of fireworks. I also was paid for several pages of curriculum ideas written for Charisma Life Publishing for their Sunday school curriculum periodicals. I led a couple of seminars on how to create a children's drama ministry and acted in a *Heaven's Gate and Hell's Flames* production. While at The Church On The Way, I got involved with a marriage seminar, deliverance ministry called Cleansing Stream Ministries, and served on the elder body praying for the sick and counseling in the prayer room.

When I moved to GA in 1999, I assisted the high school pastor at Mount Paran North Church of God, teaching Sunday School, working on drama productions, continuing to write for church skits, and acting in a few church productions. I served as an elder in that body, pastored at that time by Dr. Mark Walker, who is currently the President of Lee University in Cleveland, TN. I went on a short-term mission's trip to India, which drastically changed my perspective of the world.

From 2008 until now, my wife and I have attended

Christ the King Church in Acworth, GA, later renamed The Church at Acworth under the leadership of Jason Tomczak, son of Larry Tomczak, a well-known apostolic leader and writer. Since attending TCA, I have served as leader of a church home group. Over the years, I have studied and participated in various deliverance and inner-healing ministries (Elijah House, Beth Shalom, and SOZO). I use my prayer counseling to aid those in need of restoration. My favorite thing to do in the entire world is pray and see God work. God invades our world when we pray. It changes lives and nations.

My home group visits a local assisted-living facility, each month preaching and leading worship to serve the residents. I have been on a short-term mission trip to El Salvador, and I love one-on-one discipleship. I believe that God has given me the gift of teaching which often has a prophetic bent to it. This comes out in my writing, and I pray that God develops it further.

Being in a fast-paced sales job for 38 years, participating in church ministry, and raising four children have all been very fulfilling. However, I feel like God shifted me into a different gear recently that has amped up my desire to write. I feel I can serve others and lead them to a fuller understanding of our Savior and His will through this creative venue.

This book is a chronicle of God's goodness in the midst of my most trying times: an autobiographical treatise in the middle of a fictional adventure. I wrote this primarily so my children, grandchildren, and others I encountered over my 38-year career and ministry opportunities would be encouraged to look for God, rather than miss His guidance.

Thank you for your interest in my life pursuits. Be blessed.